BIBLIOTHECA NEERLANDICA

A Library of Dutch Classics from Holland and Belgium

REYNARD THE FOX
AND OTHER MEDIAEVAL NETHERLANDS
SECULAR LITERATURE

REYNARD THE FOX

AND OTHER MEDIAEVAL NETHERLANDS SECULAR LITERATURE

Edited and Introduced
by
E. COLLEDGE

Translated by Professor Adriaan J. Barnouw
and E. Colledge

SIJTHOFF LEYDEN / HEINEMANN LONDON
LONDON HOUSE & MAXWELL NEW YORK
1967

'Charles and Elegast', 'Walewein', 'Lancelot of Denmark' and 'Say that Again', originally published under the titles '*Karel ende Elegast*', '*Walewein*', '*Lancelot*' and '*Nu Noch*', are translated by E. Colledge; 'Reynard the Fox', originally published under the title '*Van den Vos Reinaerde*', is translated by Adriaan J. Barnouw.

Published with the aid of the Prince Bernhard Fund

First published 1967

Library of Congress Catalog Card Number 66-29434

© *A. W. Sijthoff's Uitgeversmaatschappij, N.V. 1967*

Printed in the Netherlands

CONTENTS

INTRODUCTION

In comparing the evolution of mediaeval literature in England and the Nether-lands, we must begin by conceding that much of the necessary evidence has been destroyed. For the centuries which in England mark the period between the country's christianization and the Norman Conquest, little survives for the Low Countries, and none of it deals with secular subjects; and it is beyond doubt that a new beginning was made in the twelfth century, under the inspi-ration of French courtly and chivalric poetry. But the first Netherlands man of letters of whom we know, the poet Henry van Veldeke, won great fame outside his own territories: his Aenaïs, a Dutch adaptation of Benoît de Saint-Maur's work of that name, and his courtly lyrics served as models for the Germans Gottfried of Strasbourg and Wolfram of Eschenbach, who praise him as their master. We may surmise that Henry's maturity and sure-ness of touch owe much to earlier poets in his own language whose compositions were either never written down or have since been lost. We may well think of the achievement of Hadewijch, also deeply influenced by the ideas and the forms of courtly poetry: neither she nor Henry could have attained to their eminence had they been, as is sometimes suggested, the pioneers and first experimenters in the literary use of the tongue which they so superbly employ.

Nowhere, not even in England, had the interpenetration of Romance and Germanic culture been deeper than in the southern Netherlands; and once the themes of chivalric romance and of courtly love were so introduced, a period of great excitement and literary activity followed, in which Dutch poets were able to make their own contributions to the models which they followed. It was, too, in this epoch that the multifarious political structure of the territo-ries, which delayed for so long the emergence of a unified national character, produced, in combination with the suddenly increased wealth of the great trading cities, many centres in which every art, letters included, could flourish in the patronage and sympathy which they were accorded.

It was natural that people who took uninhibited pleasure in the spectacle of opulent luxury should make a national hero of Charlemagne, who had sought to make his Western territories into another Rome or Byzantium; and this reverence for imperial splendours is clearly reflected in Charles and

7

Elegast, *the first work translated in this anthology. It was probably composed not long after Henry van Veldeke wrote; and it is an original addition to the Charlemagne epos. Its chief elements are commonplace—the King suddenly reduced from glory to wretchedness, the robber Knight whose inherent moral worth restores him to his rightful place, the exposed traitor—but their fusion is unique. The poem has been criticized because it lacks the spread and detail of other* chansons de geste, *some of them Dutch, but it is the economy and speed with which the story is told which make it outstanding. English readers will perforce be reminded by it of* Sir Gawain and the Green Knight, *but as we read here of the black knight racing through the lonely forest by the light of the moon and stars, we may well think that this poet achieves the same excitements as in* Gawain *with a less elaborate and self-conscious art. And* Charles and Elegast *has a place of its own among chivalric romances, when it introduces, in the episode of the robbery of Eggheric's castle, tension mixed with comedy in a fashion worthy of a detective story. The unhappy king with the coulter from the abandoned plough trying to pass himself off as a practised burglar is an exquisitely risible figure; and we can only regret that the poet neglected to round off his story with a traditional scene of unmasking and recognition, such as we find at the end of* Gawain, *in which the king enthroned in splendour would have to explain how, among the other adventures of this one night, he had been found ineffectually trying to break into his brother-in-law's castle.*

Here we have one of the most engaging characteristics of mediaeval art, an unselfconscious lack of set attitude, a love of the deflating surprise which the unexpected use of comedy can give. And in Charles and Elegast *we also find another theme which was to recur to the end of the Middle Ages, a thorough-going, unabashed anti-clericalism. To us today it may seem paradoxical that England and the Low Countries, famed for their religious houses and their many holy men and women, producing immense treasures of devotional literature, fostering great piety among their laity, should none the less have encouraged so much writing of this nature. But if we read these satires with attention, if we compare them with their English counterparts (*Reynard the Fox, *for instance,* with The Fox and the Wolf, Say That Again *with the jibes at ignorant clerics in* Piers Plowman*), we shall find that it is* always human weakness and folly which is being held up to ridicule, never the Christian faith or the Church or holiness. Such satirical writing was only possible among peoples who were one in faith, and who could form their own reverence for the Church's ideals, make the necessary comparisons with the shortcomings of that Church's frailer ministers. Once the Church's unity was disrupted, once the Catholic faith itself became a target to attack, such good-humoured satire was no longer possible, and instead we have, from either side, bitterness, savagery, and a lamentable uncharity.

Those who feel that Charles and Elegast is too perfunctory a treatment of its theme, with many side-issues unexplored, many loose ends still untied, would find in the immensely lengthy Walewein, of which only one short extract has been translated here, a satisfyingly epic performance. Ostensibly it is a contribution to the great Arthurian cycle. It has been thought well, here as in other places, to keep the Dutch for the hero's name, but 'Walewein' is merely a form of Wawain/Gawain; and, as in Sir Gawain and the Green Knight, the story is neatly fitted into an Arthurian frame. Often Walewein and Sir Gawain, in their resemblances, show us how enamoured both Dutch and English poets were of the atmosphere and the machinery of 'the matter of Britain'. The complete text is contained in a manuscript, now at Leyden, which was copied in A.D. 1350, and there we are told that the poem was begun by one 'Penninc' and completed by a Peter Vostaert. The introduction to this text claims that a Celtic original of the story exists, of which this is merely a translation; but this is a common device in mediaeval times (it is satirized in the prologue of Reynard the Fox), and we can be sure that this narrative is original.

When, however, we consider its separate elements, we can see that its authors rely heavily on two chief types of source, the Arthurian epic and the popular tale. We begin with Arthur and his knights, Percival, Lancelot and Kay among them, sitting at his court at Caerleon. They have dined and are now disporting themselves, when suddenly they are amazed to see a chess set come in through a window and settle upon the floor of the hall. The board is of ivory, bound in silver and set with gems, and the chessmen are of pure gold. As they gaze at it, out of the window it flies again; and Arthur promises the succession to his kingdom to the man who will follow it and obtain it for him. *After an acrimonious discussion with Kay, Walewein sets off on this adventure, and the chess set, flying before him, leads him into a perilous mountain region, where he first encounters and slays a brood of young dragons, and then their dam—infuriated on returning from foraging to discover what has happened. This, the prelude to the extract translated in this anthology, first provides us with much the same setting as in* Sir Gawain, *and then reminds us of still older literature. The fight with the dragons is clearly of the same genre as, among other celebrated examples,* Beowulf; *and Walewein's later adventures call many other types to mind. The magic bed with the singing angels which can cure the mortal wounds of any man who sleeps in it will recall the Grail cycle; the metamorphosed beasts around the castle of the King of Faerie, and Roges, the prince-turned-fox, come from the legends of the East.*

In Lancelot of Denmark *and* Say That Again *we have two strongly-contrasted examples of that dramatic art in which writers of the mediaeval Netherlands excelled. Few other aspects of European literary history have received more attention than the emergence of the secular, vernacular theatre: so much, indeed, has been written that we tend to believe that we know more about the subject than the facts warrant. How and when and why the 'mystery' plays emerged from the churches, under what circumstances the first companies of professional players were organized—these are matters about which we can still only conjecture. But the internal evidence seems to suggest that in the Low Countries the secular theatre matured faster and was professionalized sooner than in England.*

Lancelot of Denmark *is found in the Hulthem Manuscript, now in the Royal Library at Brussels, which contains a number of secular plays, probably composed in the mid-fourteenth century. It is thought that two others,* Esmoreit *and* Gloriant, *are also by the author of* Lancelot. *All these treat of romantic themes, in which the idea of true love overcoming affliction predominates. But of them,* Lancelot *is outstanding for its maturity and its realism. The principal characters are achieved with precision and economy: the evil, ruthless queen, a type greatly beloved in mediaeval legend; the weak and sensual Lancelot; Sanderijn (Alexandrina), his unhappy victim; and the noble knight with whom she finds happiness. The scene in which she uses* the image of the falcon and the flowering tree to confess her fall to the knight and place herself at his mercy is an admirable coup de théâtre; and the sureness with which the author, immediately after this, lowers the tension with the comedy supplied by the gamekeeper suggests strongly that he was writing for skilled and experienced professional performers.

Lancelot *is a direct attack upon the by now exhausted sophistications of the literature of courtly love. Unlike Guinevere's paramour, the anti-hero* Lancelot *is a despicable cad; and calculatedly the author rejects one after another of the romantic clichés. Love does alter when it alteration finds; and, if lovely woman stoops to folly, she can raise herself again, if she has the good fortune to find a decent man and the honesty not to try to hoodwink him. Like Chaucer in* Troilus and Criseyde, Lancelot *contrasts the longeurs of fashionable romance with the realities of life, and finds the truth more interesting.*

Nu Noch, Say That Again, *is theatre of a different kind, one of the many brief farces written to be played after some longer and more serious production, depending perhaps for much of its comic effect upon the spectacle of well-known actors, seen a few moments before in gallant or tragic roles, suddenly transforming themselves into knock-about comedians, designed to send the audience home in good humour. It has no subtlety whatever: this is the coarse, broad comedy of a society still close to the soil. If the reiteration of a single joke seems to us monotonous, we must try to imagine what the right player, by variation of inflexion, intonation and timing could achieve with his line, 'Say that again'.*

Perhaps one of the greatest comic achievements of all mediaeval European literature is the Dutch Reynard the Fox. *The device of attributing to animals the frailties of human beings is, in Europe, as old as Aesop, and in Asia older still; and in England it was used for such masterpieces as* The Owl and the Nightingale *and* The Nun's Priest's Tale. *But these are both miniature performances, restricted in the objects of their satire, whereas in* Reynard *we have a panorama of the life of the times, in which nothing and no one is spared the poet's wit. It has been suggested that the poem's origins and appeal are essentially bourgeois, but this is not necessarily so. The zest with which the conventions and the institutions of chivalry are mocked would surely appeal most strongly to aristocratic audiences, familiar with*

11

the way of life here satirized and best able to appreciate its subtleties. We may remember that in another mediaeval art-form often used with deadly satiric effect, the 'babooneries' and grotesque miniatures depicting all classes of society (but particularly the clergy and the aristocracy) in most unflattering guises, the finest examples which have survived are in manuscripts expressly commissioned by noble or clerical patrons. The mediaeval world had not forgotten how to laugh at itself.

An anthology planned as this has been must necessarily be not wholly representative. In particular, we shall find here none of the mediaeval Dutch lyrics of love and of nature, and nothing to convey to us the growing concern of the waning Middle Ages, in the Netherlands as elsewhere, with social and political problems. None the less, what does appear in this collection speaks of the vitality and the freshness of that rich collection of poetry which it seeks to represent, and it shows how the life of the Low Countries was then enriched, not only by their painters, sculptors, architects and musicians, but also by the poets of the Dutch tongue.

E. COLLEDGE

CHARLES AND ELEGAST

Listen to this tale, as fine as it is true, which I can tell to you. One evening Charles had laid himself down to sleep at Ingelheim upon the Rhine, for all that territory, where he was both emperor and king, belonged to him. Now listen to what happened to him there; it is both marvellous and truthful, and many are still alive who know it. He had lodged that night at Ingelheim, and he intended on the following day to wear his crown and hold his court there, for his greater glory; but as he lay and slept, a holy angel called to him, startling the king from his sleep as he said to him: 'Get up, noble sir, dress yourself as quickly as you can, arm yourself, and travel abroad to live as a robber. It is God, lord of the heavenly kingdom, who has bade me to command you so: otherwise, your life and your honour will be forfeit. Unless you set out on your robber's travels tonight, great harm will come to you; before this court which you are holding has ended, it will cost you your life, it will bring you death. Take good heed of this, and, if you will, set out as a robber. Arm yourself with spear and shield, put on your armour, mount your steed, and make no delay.'

The king listened to this, and it seemed very strange to him. Since he saw no one there who could have spoken so to him, he thought that it had all been a dream, and paid no attention to the message. The angel whom God had sent spoke again to the king, as if in anger: 'Get up, Charles, and go out to rob. It is God who commanded me to say this to you, and he has already warned you that unless you do this you will lose your life.'

With this the angel was silent; and the king cried aloud, as one in great fear: 'Alas, what can this strange thing mean? Is this some nightmare which terrifies me so, bringing such uncanny news? Oh, Lord of Heaven, what need have I to go out to steal, who am richer than any other man on earth? There is no king, there is no prince, however great his possessions be, who is not my vassal, bound to do me service. My domain is so vast that there is no other like it, and from Cologne upon the Rhine to Rome it is all mine and owns me as its emperor. Here I am lord, my wife is lady, eastwards from the wild Danube to the raging sea in the west; and I have many other possessions, Galicia and the land of Spain, which I conquered with my own hand, driving out the pagans so that the land was mine alone. Why should I need to steal, to be made wretched? Why has God ordered me to do this? I would be loth to disobey him, if I knew that this was his command; but it is hard for me to believe that it is his will that I should disgrace myself by turning robber.'

So he lay, pondering this matter in great perturbation; and he dozed off for a little while and closed his eyes, until the angel said to him once again: 'Unless you obey God's command, my lord king, you are lost, and it will cost you your life. King,' said the angel from Paradise, 'do just as you have been told, go out robbing and become a thief. This may cause you great present distress, but it will afterwards turn into joy for you.'

With these words the angel disappeared; and Charles, blessing himself at the marvellous things he had heard, said: 'These words are God's command, and I will not disobey them. I must become a thief, crime though this be, and even if I am hanged by the neck. Yet I would far rather that God would take away from me everything which I hold in fief from him, every castle, every domain, leaving me only my knight's armour. Then I could live by my shield and my spear, like a man who has nothing and goes adventuring. This would be far preferable to me to being caught as I am in this trap—to be obliged to set out at once to live as a robber, or else to disobey God. But now let him give me strength. I wish that I were safely out of this hall without any more disturbance, even if it cost me seven fine stone-built castles on the Rhine. How am I to speak of this dishonour to the knights and the lords who are lodged here in this hall? How am I to tell them that I must set out alone and unescorted into this black night, bound for a land which is strange and unknown to me?'

Saying this, Charles the king prepared himself, now that he was determined to go off stealing. He dressed in his costly garments. It was always his custom to make his people leave his arms close to the bed where he slept, those arms which were the finest that men had ever seen. Then when he was armed he walked through the palace, and there was not one of its fine doors closed, there was no gate which barred his progress. They all opened wide for him, so that he could go where he pleased. There was no one who saw him pass, for all that company lay there deep in sleep according to God's will, who did all this to guard the king, for whom divine help was always at hand. Charles crossed the drawbridge of the castle, and went without delay to the stable where he knew that he would find his horse and its saddle. He saddled and mounted it, splendid beast that it was, and rode on to the castle gate, where he saw the guard and the porter, little thinking that their lord in his armour was so close to them, sleeping soundly as God ordained. The king dismounted and opened the locked gate, and silently led his horse out.

Then King Charles sat in his saddle and said: 'God, as truly as you came upon earth, to be both Father and Son*, to redeem for all of us what Adam had lost for himself and all who were born after him: as you suffered yourself to be slain upon the Cross when the Jews had taken you prisoner, when they pierced you with a spear, when you willingly suffered this cruel death, Lord, for our need: as truly as you called Lazarus back from death as he lay shut in the tomb, as truly as you made bread from stones* and wine from water; so truly guide me in this dark night, and make your powers known to me, merciful God and Father. I confide myself wholly to you.'

He was in great doubt where he ought to go, in which direction he ought to set out on his life of crime; and so the noble Charles rode into a forest which stood close at hand. As he rode through it the moon shone brightly and the stars glittered in the heaven, all giving their clear light. And the king thought to himself: 'I used to hate thieves above all else, when I heard of them employing their cunning to rob and steal the people's goods, but now I must esteem men who live by adventuring. They know very well the risks which

* In both cases, this is what the text says.

they run: they can be deprived of their lives and their possessions, they can be hanged or beheaded or suffer crueller deaths, and their days are filled with terror. In all my time I was never content to let any man die because of a petty theft; but I drove Elegast out of my land with little cause, and since then he has often risked his life in order to gain his living. I think that he has now many cares: he has neither lands nor possessions, nor can he rely on any livelihood except what he can pick up by robbery. This is all that he has to support himself. I took away from him the land of which he was lord, which must still be a cause of great grief to him; I deprived him of castle and domain, never caring what I was doing. In his retinue he had great numbers of knights and squires, and in taking his lands and possessions I have also beggared them, who follow him still in his poverty. There is no place where they were safe from me, and it is I who deprived them of all security, leaving them neither shelter nor wages. Now they are without anything on which they can rely, and they are forced to live in wildernesses and forests, going out on the forays by which they support themselves. And yet, truth to tell, they do not steal from any poor man who lives by his own toil; and they leave the pilgrims and the pedlars in peace with their possessions. But they spare no one else: whenever they can catch bishops and canons, abbots and monks, deans and parish priests, if once such come into their power, they take their mules and their horses and knock them out of their saddles to the earth, and then they seize upon all they have brought with them, their money, their garments and their plate. So they always lurk along the ways where they know that rich men ride, and they rob them of all their treasure, their silver and their gold. They are full of cunning, and no one can catch them, though many have done their best to do so. Now, to-night, how gladly would I be one of them! Lord, God, help me to find them!'

Musing so, the king rode on, till he was aware of a horseman galloping near him as if he wanted to intercept him. His armour was as black as coal, his helmet was black, and so was the shield slung around his neck; and over his fine breastplate he wore a black tabard. The horse on which he was mounted was black, and it bore him along a side path across the forest. When the king encountered him, he blessed himself and was in dread, thinking that this black knight must be the devil, and he commended himself to Almighty God. In his heart he thought: 'Whether evil come to me or good, I shall not flee tonight from this man, and so lose my chance of adventure. And yet I know well already that this is the devil and no one else. If he were any spirit of God he would not be so black as this: everything that I can see of either horse or man is black. I fear that great harm is coming to me: and I pray God to watch over me, that this man may do me no injury.' And as he came closer, the king made the sign of the Cross again in dread, sure that this was the devil.

The black knight had now perceived the king close at hand, and he thought to himself: 'Here is someone who has missed his way, and is lost. He shall give me an account of himself, and he shall surrender to me his arms, which seem to me the finest that I have seen these seven years, set with gems and inlaid with gold shining as bright as day. How did he come into this forest? He is no poor man, armed with such weapons and riding so powerful and beautiful a horse.'

When they reached each other, they passed by with no word of greeting. Each looked closely at the other, but neither of them said a word. When the knight mounted on his black horse had ridden past the king, he reined to and pondered who the other man could be and what he was doing there. 'Why has he refused to salute me as he met me, why has he no question to put to me? I think that he has lost his way; but if I were certain that he has come here to spy upon us, intending to bring harm to me or to my people with the king whom I so dread, he would not escape tonight unscathed. If he is not searching for me, what business has he here, riding about among the trees and the undergrowth? By the Lord who made me, he shall not ride off tonight and escape me! I shall test his strength,

I will speak to him and have an answer. He may well be someone whom I can rob of his horse and everything he has on, sending him off home like a figure of fun. The bigger fool he, to come here!'

Thinking thus, he wheeled round his horse and galloped after the king; and when he overtook him, he called aloud: 'Stop, Knight! Where are you off to? I want to know what you are looking for; what is the quarry you are hunting? Be as proud as you like, measure your words as you please: before you ride any further, you will do well to answer me. I want to know who you are, and whither you are travelling at this time of night, and what your father's name was; and I will accept no excuse from you.'

The king replied: 'You want to know too much: I would rather fight you than answer you. If I were to allow you to force me to speak, I should have lived too long, letting any man compel me to tell him, against my will, what I do not wish him to know. Whether good or ill come to me, let us now decide this issue between us, and be quick about it.' (The king's shield had its cover on it, as he did not wish to carry it uncovered because of its armorial bearings. He did not want any man to know that he was the king.) After this exchange of words, they wheeled their powerful and swift horses about to face each other. They were both well armed, with mighty spears. They fought in a glade, and they rode at each other with such fury that their horses were forced to their knees. Eager for combat, they reached for their swords, and they fought for as long as a man takes to walk a mile. The black knight was strong and nimble, dangerously skilled in the arts of war, so that the king was in fear, thinking that this was the devil. He struck at the shield which the black knight resolutely held in front of him, so that it flew apart, split in two as if it were no more than a leaf from a lime tree. The black knight struck back at the king, and their swords rose and fell, thrashing down upon their helmets and their chain mail so that many a link burst asunder. Neither hauberk could withstand such blows, and the blood from their wounded flesh seeped through their chain mail. The din of battle was deafening, and the splinters flew from their shields. The helmets on their heads buckled, all notched and cracked, so sharp were their swords' edges.

In his heart the king thought: 'This is a valiant fighter, but if I tell him my name I shall be disgraced for ever, and no one will ever respect me again!' Then he struck such a blow at the black knight opposing him that he made him reel and fall from his horse, but there was still no truce between them, for the black knight struck out at the king and dealt him so violent a stroke upon his helmet that the helmet split and the knight's sword flew in two pieces: the blow was as furious as that. When the black knight saw that he had lost his sword, he said to himself: 'Alas for the day that I was born! What have I to live for now? Never once have I had good fortune, nor shall I ever have it. How can I defend myself now? I would not give two straws for my life, standing here with empty hands.'

But it seemed to the king that it would be shameful to strike down a man in such a state, and as he looked at the sword lying on the grass in two pieces, he thought: 'No one avenges his honour by striking or wounding a man who cannot protect himself.' So they stood in silence in the forest, each of them wondering greatly who the other might be.

'By the Lord who made me,' King Charles said, 'unless you tell me this one thing which I ask you, Knight, you have come to the end of your days. Tell me your name and who you are, and let us finish this fighting, for so I can ride away with honour, and I shall let you go as soon as I know what you are called.' The black knight replied: 'I am willing, if you will tell me for what reason you came here by night, and whose displeasure it is that you fear.' Then the noble Charles said: 'First answer me, and then I shall tell you what I am seeking here and hunting for, and why it is that I dare not ride by day. It is for no idle fancy of mine that you see me armed like this; and I shall tell you how it has happened, as soon as you tell me your name—be sure of that.'

'Sir,' Knight Elegast replied at once, 'I have had but evil fortune. I have lost the possessions and the lands which once I owned, through ill luck, as happens to many a man. If I were to tell you all my tale, it would seem far too long to you before ever I had finished, so many misfortunes have befallen me.' When the king heard this, he was as joyful as if he owned every treasure that is shipped along the Rhine: and he said: 'Knight, if it be your pleasure, tell me now your name, and how you live. By all that God holds dear, and by the great God himself, you need have no fear of me; and I shall answer any question that you put to me, without any strife or hostility, once you have told me what I ask; and you may be sure of this.'

'Sir, I am called Elegast, and I will not conceal from you that I have to steal to live. But let me tell you this: I steal from no poor man who lives by his own toil. Whatever a pilgrim or a pedlar has I leave him to enjoy, but I spare no one else. In all the days of my life, since I lost the possessions on which I should have lived, when King Charles drove me out of my lands—I will tell you this, disgraceful though it be—I have dwelt in wildernesses and forests with twelve companions, and it is the rich who have to support us. Bishops and canons, abbots and monks, deacons and parish priests —whenever I can catch them, I know how to get their goods. If they have treasure, however well locked the chest may be, I get my hands upon it and I share it with my fellows. What more should I tell you? I am cunning in many arts, and my companions are here in the forest. I came out looking for adventure, and I found it, no mistake, for I have lost my sword, and I would give any treasure in the world to have it back unbroken in my hand; and I have received my share of blows, more than I ever received from any one man in a single night. Now tell me, Knight, what is your name, and who is your enemy? Is he a man of so great power that you are forced to ride by night? Cannot you overcome your enemies, you who are so valiant a warrior?'

The king thought to himself: 'God has heard my prayer. Now I must act warily. This is the man whom I wanted, more than anyone upon earth, to ride with tonight, and God has brought me so far;

but now necessity forces me to tell lies.' 'By the Lord who can command me,' the king said to Elegast, 'you will have a trusty companion in me, and I offer you firm friendship and good will. But I must tell you how I live, for there can be no deception between friends. I have stolen so much treasure that if I were to be caught with the half of it, they would not let me ransom myself with my own weight in red gold. But it was through necessity that I did this, necessity which knows no law.'

'Then tell me, Knight, who are you?'

'I will tell you my name, since that is your pleasure. I am called Adelbrecht, and it is my custom to break God's law by stealing from churches and monasteries, and every other holy place. I steal goods of every sort, and I leave no one in peace—rich or poor, I pay no heed to their entreaties. There is no man so poor that I cannot profit from him; and it is my delight to take what is his, never to give him anything of mine. This is how I have lived; and recently I have been plotting to seize a treasure which I know about, and which will soon be mine. If I had some trusty help, before tomorrow dawns, I could have as much as I wanted and as my horse could carry. The treasure was ill gotten, and God would not punish us for taking some of it. It is laid up in a castle in a region I know well; and if we had five hundred pounds of it, it would do little harm to the man we robbed. Let us go off together tonight, and what we can capture between now and daybreak I will divide, and you shall choose your share, and we shall both be satisfied.'

Said Elegast, 'Where is this treasure? Tell me that, my dear friend: in what place is it, where am I to go? I shall not take one step after you until I know.' Then the noble Charles replied: 'I will tell you all. The king has so much treasure that it can do him little harm to take some from where it is lying.' When the king said that he intended to rob himself, Elegast did not remain silent. 'God forbid!' he said. 'The man is not living who can persuade me to do the king an injury. Even though he followed evil counsel, taking my possessions and driving me out, I shall still do all I can, so long as I live, to be his good friend. I will not go robbing him by night, for he is the lawful ruler. If I offered him anything but respect, I should be blameworthy before God, and there is no one who shall force me to do this.'

When the king heard this, he rejoiced in his heart to know that Elegast the thief wished him well and loved him; and he thought that if without loss of honour he could return home, he would give Elegast so much in possessions that he would be able to live honourably for the rest of his life, without stealing and robbing. This was truly his intention; and after he had so reflected, he asked Elegast if he could take him off somewhere else, where that night they could both seize upon some booty. If Elegast would allow him to come along, he would do his best, with all the skill he possessed.

'Yes, gladly,' said Elegast, 'if I can be sure that you are not making sport of me. There is Eggheric of Egmond, who is married to the king's sister: we can steal from him without any sin. It is a pity that he is alive, for he has betrayed many and brought great harm to them. If he could have his own way he would rob the king his lord of life and honour, as I know well; and this even though he has received many great gifts, castles and treasures, from him. Though we were to take from him his last resources, we should be doing little wrong in robbing him. If you choose, let us go there.'

The king pondered and was silent as he heard this plan disclosed for where they were to go stealing; and he reflected that even if his sister were to capture him, she would never let them hang him. So they made this compact to go off alone and to rob Eggheric of his treasure, and the king took careful note of all this.

They came riding on their fine horses into a plain, and there they found a plough standing. The king at once dismounted, and Elegast rode on by the path which they were taking. The king took hold of the coulter which he found in the plough, and thought to himself, 'This will be useful for our enterprise. Those who intend to break into castles need to provide themselves with the necessary tools.' So he mounted again with no delay, and spurred on his horse

24

to follow Elegast, who now was some way ahead. Listen to what I shall tell you now. When they arrived in front of the fortress, which was the finest and the best which stood anywhere upon the Rhine, Elegast said: 'This is the place. Now, tell me, Adelbrecht, what do you think that we should do? I will be guided by your advice. I should be sorry if harm came to you, so that people could say "It was all the fault of the other man".'

To this the king replied: 'I was never inside the castle or the keep, so far as I know. I could easily make a mistake if I were to go inside. I shall have to rely on you.' Elegast answered: 'I am agreed, provided that you are an accomplished thief, and that I shall soon know. Let us not lose any time in making an opening in the castle wall to creep through.' They both agreed, and quickly tethered their horses, then noiselessly approached the wall. Elegast produced a pick with which to attack it, and the king drew out the coulter from the plough. Elegast stood there laughing, and asked where he had had it made. 'If I could find the smith's house, I would have another made for me. I have never seen such a tool used for this mining work.' The king replied: 'That may well be so. Three days ago, when I was riding alongside the Rhine, I had to leave my pick behind, because it fell down on the road, and there were people following me, so that I did not dare go back for it, in case they mocked me. So there I was without my pick, but I found this by moonlight on a plough.' Elegast said: 'It will serve its turn, if we get in here tonight; and afterwards you can have another pick made.' So they stopped talking and worked at the opening; and Elegast, whose limbs were practised in such work, did better than the king, who, even though he was tall and strong, had no experience of these tasks. When they had made an opening right through the wall, and were ready to go in, Elegast said: 'You wait outside to collect what I bring out.' He would not allow the king to go inside, for what he had seen of his lack of skill convinced him that Charles was no practised thief; yet none the less, whatever happened, he intended to share his winnings with him. So the king stayed there, and Elegast went inside; and he had all the skills which he had exercised in many places, and he was just the man for the task. He took a herb from a jar and put it into his mouth, for anyone doing so can understand what the cocks crow and the dogs bark to one another; and so he heard a cock and a dog, speaking their lingua franca and saying that the king was standing outside the castle. Elegast said to himself: 'How can this be? If the king were outside, I think I should be in harm's way. It seems to me that I have been either betrayed or led astray by some hobgoblin.' He went back to where he had left the king, and told him what he had heard, if he could trust his own senses:that a cock and a dog had said in their own language that the king was thereabouts, but that they did not know how close he was.

Then the noble Charles said: 'And what answer did you give them? What would the king be doing here? If you are going to believe in the cackling of hens and the yapping of mongrels, you will believe everything you hear. I think that you are stuffing me with old wives' tales. Why are you trying to frighten me? You should have more sense than to believe such nonsense.' 'Very well—listen yourself,' said Elegast; and he plucked a herb growing in front of them, and put it into the king's mouth, and said: 'You will hear for yourself—this is what I did before.' And then the cock crowed again, and said what it had previously said, that the king was there, but that it did not know how close to the castle he was. 'My friend,' said Elegast, 'if what the cock crows is true, if the king is anywhere at hand, there is a rope around my neck!' 'Rubbish, my friend!' Charles replied. 'Are you frightened out of your wits? I thought that you would show better sense. Let us get on with it, even though they catch us now.' 'I will make a start,' said Elegast, 'and let us see what you gain by it.' He asked for the herb back again, but it was not in the king's mouth, nor could he find it anywhere on the ground. It was not to be found, and the king said: 'What has happened? I think that I have lost my herb, which I was holding clenched between my teeth. Upon my faith, I am sorry for this!'

Elegast laughed, and said: 'Are you a felon, or are you not? It a-mazes me that you do not get killed every time you go out stealing: you should have been dead a long time ago. My dear friend'—he was quite open about it—'I stole your herb. You do not know the first thing about stealing!' The king thought to himself, 'How right you are!', but that was the end of their conversation; and he commended himself to God and asked for his protection, for he was by no means free from fear. But Elegast knew many cunning arts, and, using them, he made everyone in the castle fall asleep, and at one stroke caused every lock, small or great, which they had locked with keys to fly open; and so he went straight to where the treasure was lying, before anyone heard or saw what he was doing, and he brought back with him as much as he pleased. Then Charles wanted to ride off, but Elegast told him to wait, for he wanted to go back for a saddle which was placed in the room in which Eggheric and his wife were asleep, the finest that anyone ever saw. There is no man alive who could properly describe to you the splendour of that saddle: its pommel alone beggared description, hung with a hundred great bells, all of red gold, to jingle as Eggheric rode. 'Just wait now, my friend: I shall steal his saddle from him, even if they hang me by the neck for it.'

This did not please the king at all. He would rather have forgone the stealing of the saddle, if only Elegast had not gone in again. And when Elegast found this saddle which I have just been describing to you, its bells set up such a jingling that Eggheric started out of his sleep and said: 'Who is after my saddle?' He would have seized hold of his sword, had his wife not prevented him, asking him what he thought he was fighting, what evil spirits were deceiving him. She took the sword in its scabbard from him, and said: 'No one can possibly have got in here. It is something else which has alarmed you'; and she insisted that he should tell her what was troubling his mind so that, as she had seen, he had not been able to sleep for three whole nights, had not been able to eat for three whole days. She pressed him to tell her this; and women, whether they be young or old, are full of such guile. She persisted with him till at last he began to tell her that he had sworn to kill the king, and that those who were appointed to do it would soon be at hand; and he gave her all the names of those who were to be the king's murderers.

Elegast listened to all this and took careful note of it; and he determined that he would expose this monstrous and treacherous plot.

Eggheric's wife said: 'I would rather by far that they hanged you by the neck than that I should connive at such a thing!' and with this Eggheric struck his wife such a blow in the face that blood gushed from her nose and mouth, and she reared herself up and thrust her head out over the frame of the bed. AfterwardsElegast told the king how he was there, watching all this, and how he had crept softly up, and caught some of her blood in his right glove as it fell, so that he could bring it to the king as a sign that he should be on his guard. Then Elegast uttered a spell, which made everyone around fall asleep, and he repeated it until Eggheric and his wife were sleeping soundly; and then Elegast stole from him his saddle and his sword, which he so greatly prized, and made off with them, out of the castle to the place where he had left his horse, and to the king, who was in great anxiety. He did not care how much treasure Elegast was bringing; if he could have had his will, he would not have stayed so long, so greatly was he troubled. He asked Elegast where he had been all that time; but Elegast replied: 'It is not my fault. By all that God has given life, the wonder is that my heart has not broken for the sorrow that has seized upon it. If my heart can suffer this, it will never break for any other woe in the world, of that I am certain, for no other will ever equal this. My friend,' he said, 'this is the saddle I just told you about. Hold it for me, for I am going back to cut off Eggheric's head, or else I shall stab him to death with my knife as he lies sleeping with his wife. I will not be dissuaded for all the gold that there is in the world; and I shall return to you at once.'

Then the king entreated him greatly to tell him what it was which had so distressed him: 'Here you are, safe and sound, and you have at least a thousand pounds in gold, and the saddle which you went back for!' 'Ah, God, it is something quite different which oppresses my heart and consumes my unhappy mind. Now I have lost my liege lord. Hitherto I was confident that I would regain my fortune and better my state of beggary; but tomorrow early my lord is to die, and I can tell you how it will be: Eggheric has sworn to kill him.'

Then Charles perceived very clearly that God had commanded him to go out stealing so as to preserve him from death, and fervently he thanked the Lord of Heaven for this; and then he said to Elegast: 'How do you expect to prevent it like this? If you stab him with a knife whilst he is in bed with his wife, that will arouse the whole court, and then you would need more than good luck if you were not to ruin everything and bring your own life to an end. If the king dies, well then, he is dead, and there is no more to be said about it; and you will recover from your grief!' The king said this deliberately to test Elegast, but he had also another object, for he greatly wanted to make off from this place, in which he hated to stay any longer. Elegast replied at once: 'By all that God has made, if I had not sworn friendship with you, you would pay this very night for what you have said against my lord King Charles, whom every man ought to revere. By the Lord who made me, I shall carry out my enterprise and avenge my sufferings on those who have sworn to kill the king before I leave this castle, whether good or ill come to me.'

The king thought to himself: 'This man is my friend, however ill I have deserved of him. I shall atone for that if I am spared, and he will have recompense for all his misfortunes.' Then to Elegast he said: 'My friend, I can give you better advice on how to bring this Eggheric of Egmond to book. As soon as it is day, ride off to where the king is, and tell everything to him and reveal what monstrous deed is planned. When he hears what you have to say, that will make peace between you, and your reward will be great. You will ride beside the king every day of your life, as if you were his own brother, for as long as God spares you.'

Elegast said: 'No, whatever happens, I shall never appear before the king. He is my bitter enemy, because once I robbed him, from his treasure, of more than two strong horses could carry. I shall never let him set eyes on me by night or by day, and you are wasting your words.' But the noble Charles said: 'I shall tell you what to do. Ride off to your own stronghold, where you left your companions, and do as I advise you—take our booty with you, and tomorrow when it is day we shall divide it between us in peace, and meanwhile I shall go to the king—I know where he is—and tell him about this business, for I should be sorry if they were to kill him.'

So saying, they separated. Elegast went off to join his men in the stronghold where he had left them, and the noble Charles rode to his castle at Ingelheim. His heart was sorely oppressed because the man who by rights ought to have stood loyally by him wanted to betray him. The castle gate still stood wide open, and all his people lay fast asleep. He shut up his horse in its stall, and went to his bed-chamber. Before anyone had heard or seen him, he had taken off his armour. Then the watchman arose, and mounting the high battlement he blew on his horn to announce the new day which now was dawning; and all the men whom God had made to sleep whilst the king stole forth awakened again in the castle which had sheltered them so well. Then King Charles sent for one of his retinue, and held secret counsel with him, and told him all that had happened: how he knew without any doubt that Eggheric of Egmond had sworn to kill him, and would soon advance upon him with his whole army in order to disgrace him and take his life; and he asked his retinue to give him good counsel, so that he might preserve his honour and they their rightful lord.

The Duke of Bavaria then said: 'Let them come. They will find us here, and many of them will pay for this with their lives. I know what is best for us to do. There is many a valiant Frenchman here from France and from Valois, many knights and many men-at-arms who came to this land with you. Let them arm themselves at once and assemble in the great hall; and you, their king, stand armed in the middle of them all. Then if anyone tries to kill you or harm you, we shall know how to repulse him: his own blood will flow down over his spurs; and Eggheric will be the first to suffer.'

This counsel seemed good to them all, and they armed themselves at once, everyone who had heart for the fight and could carry weapons, both the humble and the great. They expected a stern conflict, for Eggheric had a great force, and every lord of any domain along the banks of the Rhine would come to his assistance. At the gate they posted sixty men, armed and helmeted; and when Eggheric's retinue came galloping up to attack the king's court, they opened the gates wide and let them all ride in; but when they were in the courtyard the defenders tore off the men's outer garments and revealed that they were all armed in metal breastplates and with sharp weapons. It was plain that they were intent upon evil. As each troop rode in, they were overpowered and taken prisoner; and Eggheric himself rode up, accompanied by the last troop of all, he who was responsible for this whole murderous attack. He dismounted, intending to proceed to the hall; but then all the doors were closed at once, and he and his men, who were better armed than any of the others had been, were taken captive in their turn. Eggheric was led into the palace before his lord, the king; and he might well be filled with shame. The king reproached him greatly, but Eggheric denied his accusations, and would not admit his crime; and he said: 'My lord the king, be better advised. If you condemn me who have not deserved this, it will cost you many a friend. Neither you nor any of your barons dare say to me that I have betrayed you. If anyone here wants to say that to me, I will make him take it back with my sword or my spear-point: so, if anyone pleases, let him step forward now!'

When the king heard this he laughed to himself; he sent a troop of messengers to find Elegast in his hiding place in the forest, and tell him that the king bade him to come to him quickly, that he forgave him all his crimes, and promised to make him a rich man if he would act as champion against Eggheric. The messengers made no delay, and they fulfilled all the king's commands. They hastened to find Elegast, and they repeated to him all that the king had said; and when he heard it he rejoiced greatly. As soon as he had heard their news, he ordered his horse to be made ready at once, and to be fitted with the saddle which he had stolen from Eggheric; and he swore, as he was a Christian, that if God would grant him one prayer he would ask for nothing else: only let him be allowed to fight for the honour of his liege lord.

They returned with great speed; and when the good knight Elegast entered the king's hall, this is what he said: 'God keep all this company, the king and all I find here with him! But for Eggheric I have no greeting. God, who let himself be crucified for our sake, is very mighty, and it is that sweet maid Mary whose prayers have preserved me to see this day, when they will hang Eggheric of Egmond high upon a gallows for the winds to sport with. If it were possible for God to sin, he would have sinned in letting Eggheric escape till now; for without any cause or need he has sworn to kill my lord!'

When Elegast had said this, Eggheric would dearly have liked to avenge it, but he was powerless to do so, for there were many there to restrain him; and the king replied: 'Welcome to my court! Now I admonish you, in the name of all who pray to God for forgiveness of their sins, that you make known without concealment the murder plotted by Eggheric, whom you see here. Be afraid of no one: speak the truth, and only the truth, about the adventure which you had.'

'Gladly,' said Elegast, 'I have nothing to conceal. I know very well that Eggheric swore to kill you. I heard him say it as he lay in bed, and he dealt his wife such a blow for gainsaying him that her mouth and her nose ran with blood. She rose in the bed and leaned her head out over the frame; and I was there and saw what happened, and I stole up quickly and caught some of the lady's blood in my right glove'—and he showed the glove to the king and to all the others who wanted to look at it. 'If Eggheric were to dare to say that I am lying, I would make him suffer for it before the sun went down,* in single combat; or else I would forfeit my life.' To which Eggheric replied: 'I refuse to be disgraced, nor shall anyone ever put it about that I engaged in combat with an outlawed thief: I will answer for that upon my life. This man would do better to fight with churls, rather than challenge me.' And the other answered: 'Sir Eggheric, it is true that I am no duke, as you are, and I was once outlawed, when the king deprived me of my riches because I fell from his favour; but I have never been a murderer or a traitor. I have taken much of their riches away from wealthy men, but it was necessity and poverty which forced me to do this. You, however, are a murderer,** and you cannot refuse to fight with any man in the world who chooses to challenge you for your crimes.'

To this the king rejoined: 'Upon my oath, you speak the truth. If I acted justly towards him, I would tell one of my grooms to haul him out and hang him by the throat.' Then it was all up with Eggheric, and he thought to himself, when he saw how matters stood: 'I had rather fight than let myself be hanged.' In the whole court there was no one who dared to speak up for him. So the combat was arranged; the king commanded his barons to see that both men were at the place of conflict, armed, soon after the nones. The king intended to be present himself, and he ordered the lists to be made ready, and he prayed that God would decide justly in the outcome of the battle. The king spoke encouraging words to Elegast, and said that if he fought successfully and preserved his own life, he would give him his sister, whom Eggheric, who had sworn to kill him, had wedded, as his wife.

They roped off the place of battle and posted many armed men

* At this point there is a gap in the Dutch text, which Kloeke in his edition has supplied from the mediaeval German poem *Karl Meinet*, the author of which used a now lost but complete text of *Charles and Elegast*.
** Here the Dutch text resumes.

around it; and shortly before the hour for vespers Elegast rode first into the lists, because he was the challenger. He dismounted upon the grass, and feel upon his knees in prayer, and said: 'God, for your mercifulness I entreat you today for pardon for all the misdeeds which I have ever committed. I acknowledge them all truly, but, gentle God, who are all-powerful, do not take vengeance upon me for my sins today! By your five sacred wounds which you received for our wrongdoings, protect me today, so that I do not perish and am not defeated. If I am not laid low by my sins, I hope to come out of this well. God who are all perfection, by your great power let me win; and you, sweet lady Mary, you I swear to serve faithfully, and never again in all my life to live as robber or thief in the wildernesses and forests, if I can save my life now.'

When he had finished his prayer, he made the sign of the Cross over his whole body, and with his right hand he traced that fair sign over his knight's armour and over the horse which stood before him; and he entreated God's mercy, that he might honourably bear himself and emerge safe from the battle. When he had said this, he mounted in his armour, and slung his shield on his left side. Now a great conflict was at hand: he took his spear in his hand, and Eggheric approached, splendidly armed, lusting for fight and with his heart full of anger. He spoke no word, he made no prayer to God; but he struck at his horse with his spurs, and rode at Elegast, who, galloping towards him, thrust furiously through the leather of Eggheric's cuirass, so that he fell from his horse on to the earth. Eggheric seized his sword from its scabbard, and said: 'I will kill the pair of you, Elegast, you and your horse, unless you dismount at once. If you do, your horse may go free: it is so great and powerful a beast it would be a pity for me to kill it, and many would lament it. Even if you cannot save your own life, at least spare your horse.'

Angrily Elegast answered: 'If you were not on foot, I would make a quick end of this fight, but I will not kill a horseless man. I will show you generosity, even though it may be to my disadvantage. Mount your horse again, and let us fight as knights. I would rather have men's good esteem than kill you unfairly, even though this prolong the fight.'

King Charles was grieved that Elegast delayed in this way, sparing Eggheric, who, at Elegast's words, caught his horse and mounted in the saddle; and the battle began again, and lasted till long after vespers. None who watched it had ever seen such a furious conflict as there was between these two: and this is the very truth. Then said the King of France: 'God, you who are all-powerful, put an end to this battle, and decide justly in this long conflict!' Elegast was armed with a sword which was worth his own weight in red gold, which would serve any man in his need: the king had given it to him. Elegast now raised it, and with it he struck so great a blow,* by the help of our Lord God, who heard the king's prayer and guarded over Elegast, giving him his most powerful aid, that Eggheric fell out of his saddle. The king watched this, and said: 'Very God, ruling us from above, rightly must I praise you for your justice and your grace towards me. Those who serve you are wise, for you can help them, and you give your aid to all who entreat you for grace. Now will I put an end to this affair.' They dragged Eggheric away, and hanged him, and all those who had come with him, and they were spared for no prayer or entreaty.

Elegast's honour had been preserved, and for this he thanked our Lord. The king bestowed Eggheric's wife on him, and they lived all their lives together in concord. So God will order all our affairs well before the day of our death; and may the heavenly Father grant this to us all: and to this let every man say 'Amen'.

* The rest of the poem is wanting in the Dutch text, and Kloeke has supplied it from *Karl Meinet*.

WALEWEIN

The Fight with the Dragon:
The King of Faerie's Castle
(ll. 500–825)

So Walewein could not move from there, because the two of them were so closely entwined that neither of them could break free or shift one way or the other; and Walewein could scarcely speak, so tight was the dragon's tail twined round about him. The dragon was threatening his life, dashing him, caught in its tail, again and again upon the ground, constantly renewing its attacks, and thrusting him into a crevice where he could barely cry aloud or move. Then it seized upon Walewein's weapon with its claws, and tightened the grip of its tail upon him, so that it seemed that he could never escape from this peril; and when Walewein freed one hand—there is no word of this untrue—and reached for the sword at his side, it was gone. Never before, and never again in all his life, was Walewein in such straits, and he thought that his last hour had come: but suddenly his hand came upon his dagger, and he rejoiced, and he thanked God who had not left him powerless. Then the bold Walewein unsheathed the dagger and stabbed at the dragon again and again, but this was of little avail, for it hardly injured the dragon; and had it been able to hold its head out of reach, Walewein could never have pierced or killed it. But the spear which he had splintered in the dragon's throat acted as a bit between its jaws, and helped him now, as, in agony, hardly able to move his one free hand, he took the dagger and struck down its throat, right into its belly, piercing its heart. The dragon shrieked in its death agony, and Walewein lay in great peril under its feet, as its blood, hotter than any fire, came pouring out on him from its wound. He said: 'This is no beast—this is the devil, come from Hell to destroy me; no one but he could afflict me so. I have killed it, and still I cannot free myself of it. However great my strength might be, this devil has trapped me so tight that I shall be cooked alive in the blood from its wounds, which feels hotter than fire to me.' So he lay there, in the crevice, underneath the beast, almost drowning in its blood; and so it seemed that it would kill him, until Walewein seized the dagger and plucked it out and hacked at the dragon's tail, until in the end he cut himself loose and freed himself from the torment which it had inflicted on him.

39

Thanks be to God that he escaped; and with a joyful heart he did thank God in his heaven above. He was full of joy as he saw the dragon lying there dead which had done him such harm, and which at last he had escaped. He said: 'I shall not need to worry whether one fine day you will do injury to some other man. Never, I trust, will you succeed in that; and to make sure I shall cut off your feet.' This he did at once, and when it was done, he said: 'Now I trust in the Lord that you will never again offer to anyone the violence which you once used. My trusty breastplate, in which I have so often ventured forth, could not resist your attack, it was not proof against you: you pierced it and exposed my body, and through the holes you gave me one deep wound after another in my side.' Walewein was filled with sorrow and joy: greatly rejoicing that he had killed the dragon, but on the other hand very grieved that he had lost his sword. And he was deprived, too, of his shield, even though that might cost him his life: it lay smashed to pieces beneath the dragon; but he was well avenged for this. His spear, too, was shattered in two, and never would he wield it again; and his horse Gringolet had run away, so that he had to stand there all alone, in danger of his life, and bleeding from fifteen separate wounds that the dragon had inflicted on him.

So his hardships were very great; yet Walewein had no time to heed the sufferings and harm that the dragon had caused him. Had he known what would befall him, he would have wished that he had never in all his life heard of the chess set he was seeking. So he wandered all about the mountain, searching for what he might find, and finding many strange chances, and so he chanced to discover his good sword, which he so greatly loved and prized. Rejoicing, he picked it up, and was quick to thrust it back into the scabbard which he still had at his side. Shaking and groaning from the pain of his wounds, at last he found a pass in the mountain side, and as he stood there where it opened out, he saw a fair countryside spread before him, and at that moment Gringolet saw his master and galloped up to him as fast as he could. The horse, too, had been injured in the fight, in which the dragon had clawed him in many places.

Now hear what Walewein did next: he sat down and tended the many wounds which he found all over his body. They say that nowhere could he find bandages and ointment, though he needed them more than any man alive; nor was there any water for him there. All he could do was to cleanse his wounds with blood, and to bind them up, each one as he came upon it. When he had done this, he got up again and walked to his horse; but when he looked down the mountain-side, it seemed to him that he was so high up that no one could have shot an arrow from a bow from the bottom of the valley up to where he stood. How was he to descend, he and his horse Gringolet? For the mountain was so formed that no human soul who was up there could ever come down without falling, plunging into the water whichever way he fell. A river flowed all round the foot of the mountain, great and wide and deep, and the mountain leapt sheer up out of the river, and its huge and mighty rocks looked to him like a dungeon. In the mountainside was this ravine, where the dragon often used to repair, and where it had made its lair, for it did not want any man to come near it; and so it was hard indeed to come in or out. Walewein now rued that he had ever come to the mountain, and there is no wonder that he was sore at heart, for the dragon had been a cruel adversary. But good fortune had attended his adventures until then, and that gave him courage. He said: 'I have escaped the perils which the dragon threatened, even though I still fear greatly for my life, lest I fall headlong down from this mountain into the river. But a man is better off fighting than dead; and if I stay here for the rest of my life, I cannot think what I shall eat or drink.'

So he began to consider that he must risk his life again. 'If I am to die, I will at least get down to where men can know about it. There would be little profit to me in dying here,' the hero said, 'because no one would ever know what had become of me.' So, in great anxiety, he went to his horse Gringolet, and grasped the bri-

dle and mounted; but as he looked around him, Gringolet caught
sight of the river and leapt down towards it, and then there was no
turning back for them. You may well believe me, if he had been the
lord of Paris, he would gladly have given it all to have been safe
back at home in Caerleon. He kept his seat on his precious steed, as
he had great need to do; and it seemed an age until they both
plunged into the river and Gringolet struck out swimming. Now
at last Walewein was able to cleanse his body, wounded and bloody
in every limb; and Gringolet grew very weary of swimming, but
though exhausted kept on, till, at last feeling land under its hooves,
the horse stood and rested itself upon an island in the river, with
only its head above the water. Walewein might well count himself
fortunate in his good horse, for truly it had served him well. Then
Gringolet swam on to the opposite bank, and then Walewein found
himself in a fair pasture, and he sat down on the green sward to rest
his weary body, wounded in so many places in his cruel combat;
and Gringolet showed the marks of it too, lying there as if dead.
Walewein felt great pity for the beast, and pulled up handfuls of the
grass and went over with it to his horse; and he began to stroke it
and rub it, hoping that it was not going to die. When it sprang to
its feet and stood at his side, Walewein was full of joy. But if anyone had wished to attack him then, he would have had nothing to
defend himself with: he had neither shield nor spear with which to
guard himself, had there been need. Yet, emptyhanded as he was,
still he was full of courage. Through the many gashes the dragon
had inflicted on his armour, his fair body could be seen; and so he
stood there all alone at the side of Gringolet his steed, until he
seized the bridle and mounted. The knight was heavy of heart, for
he could see no path which he could follow; and so he rode up
and down the lovely meadow, until he was sure that he could not
find a way. He did not give up, however, and presently it seemed to
him that he saw before him a castle, all shining as if it were made of
gold. Walewein thought that he would try to gain shelter there, and
as soon as he had formed this intention he spurred his horse on in

that direction. The castle seemed to stand in a moat, and above it a banner had been hoisted. The King of Faerie lived there; and do you know why he was called 'of Faerie'? I shall tell you, never fear: he was so called because he transformed men into every kind of beast that lives on land or in water, or else into birds of every kind that ever flies.

I do not think that anywhere in the world is there a finer castle than this. It was not made of mortar and stone, yet no such castle could be fairer; and all around it in letters of gold there was written for all to read: 'Let no man approach this castle. The moat around it is half a mile wide. Let no man come near this castle which the king has built, but let each man keep his distance.' But Walewein had pursued the road which brought him to the gates, and greatly he wondered, as he drew near the castle, to see a huge collection of animals of every kind, those whom the king had transformed. He left his steed standing below, and came into the castle on foot; and there he found the King of Faerie, and his son Alexander, at either side of the chess board, playing with the chessmen which had cost him so much sorrow. Then Walewein was happier than he had been for many a day, for he saw that he had found at last the chessmen which he had sought so long and for which he had suffered so much. So he approached and greeted the king and the young lord, his son; and courteously they returned his greeting, and rose from their game of chess, and made the Knight Walewein welcome.

REYNARD THE FOX

Translated by
Adriaan J. Barnouw

INTRODUCTION

On Monday 12 September 1938, a simple ceremony took place at Hulst, a little Dutch town near the Belgian border, where Dutchmen and Belgians joined in unveiling a monument to a thirteenth-century Flemish poet. It does not show him in effigy, for no one knows who or what he was. He may have been a monk, he may have been a law clerk, he may have been a learned burgher. We only know that his name was Willem, for so he tells us in the opening line of his poem. But there were any number of Willems in the Flanders of his day. Without some supplementary knowledge it is impossible to identify him. If he had added to his name some further particulars such as the name of his father, the place where he lived, the profession he followed, the nickname his neighbours gave him, we might be able to reconstruct a faint picture of the type of man he was.

What, then, can one make of a monument erected to the memory of an unknown worthy? The cenotaph of the Unknown Soldier belongs in another category: to everyone who lost a son or husband on the battlefield he is a clearly defined symbol. But no one possesses a mental picture of the poet who was honoured at Hulst. We can, of course, construct an imaginative statue of the man from the character traits that his poem reveals. He was a wit and a humorist, he belonged to the burgher class, and shared its hatred of feudal arrogance and prerogatives. But the sculptor did better than that. He honoured the unknown poet in his hero. For the lineaments of that hero are familiar to everyone. He is as much an abstraction as is the Unknown Soldier. He is the embodiment of sly wit that triumphs over brute force, a mediaeval symbol of burgher foxiness. In short, he is the Fox, and his name is Reynard.

The poetic vogue of Reynard the Fox was limited in time and space. His literary habitat was Alsace and Lorraine, the North of France, and the Netherlands from, roughly speaking, the early twelfth century till the end of the fourteenth. He does not seem to have gained epic fame in England. There exists, it is true, a short poem in southern English, of The Fox and the Wolf, *in which the stronger of the two is of course made the other's dupe. It was written in the second quarter of the thirteenth century, about 150 years before a nameless Nun's Priest entertained his fellow pilgrims on the road to*

47

Canterbury with the merry tale of the Cock and the Fox. In those two stories occur the only appearances of the fox in the mediaeval poetry of England.* *They prove acquaintance on the part of the poets with some branches of the French* Roman de Renart; *their rarity makes one suspect that Reynard did not live in the oral tradition of English folk tales. His very name was evidently not current among English people. In the* Nun's Priest's Tale *he is called Russell, a name that belongs, in the* Roman de Renart, *to one of Reynard's sons. Only once in all his poetry does Chaucer show that he knew the name of Reynard. In the* Legend of Good Women *he says of Demophon, the faithless lover of Queen Phillis, that he was*

> *false of love; it com hym of nature*
> *As doth the fox Renard, the foxes sone.*

But the passing reference proves no intimate knowledge of the French beast epic. On the contrary, the poet seems to have known the fox's literary family so superficially that he confused the names of father and son.

In France and the Low Countries, on the other hand, the names of the animals that figure prominently in the Reynard story had currency among all classes. The most convincing proof of that is the name of the hero in French. For Renard, *the fox's proper name in the epic, became in course of time his generic name, and* goupil, *the original word for 'fox', went out of use.*

The region of the beast epic's vogue formed a borderland between Romance and Germanic cultures, and the names of the beasts reflect that bilingual origin. Reynard, Isengrim, Bruin, Grimbert, Tybert are unmistakably Dutch; Noble, Coward, Beline, Chanticleer were christened on the French side of the border.

Did popular parlance invent those names? It does not seem likely. They were probably coined by the learned monks who were the first to turn the beasts into epic heroes. The earliest occurrence, as far as I know, of the name

---

* R. M. Wilson, in Early Middle English Literature, *pp. 243 ff, has collected evidence of a few other animal stories that once existed in English but which have not been preserved, and Kenneth Sisam, in his edition of* The Nun's Priest's Tale *reproduces some misericords illustrating the chase of the fox. But a Reynard epic that could compare with Willem's Flemish poem and its French models does not seem to have existed.*

Isengrim is in the autobiography of Guibert, abbot of the monastery of No-gent, which was written between the years 1114 and 1117. In his third book he recounts the murder of Galdricus, or Waldric, Bishop of Laon, who had made himself hated among the people of his diocese. One day they invaded his palace. The bishop fled into the cellar and hid in a barrel. But Teudegald, the ringleader of the mob, discovered him there. This fellow knew that Galdricus had given him the nickname Isengrim, and when he had the prelate in his power he retaliated in coin: 'Is Sir Isengrim resting here?' he asked derisive-ly, pulled Galdricus by his hair from the cask and beat him up.

It does not follow from Guibert's story that Teudegald knew the meaning of the nickname. Guibert, in any case, found it necessary to explain it: 'For thus the wolves are called by certain persons'. Not by the common people, apparently, but by men of letters. The beast epic in the vernacular had Latin precursors, and the names of the beasts occur in Latin forms before they crop up in French, German and Dutch.

It is no mere accident, I believe, that the wolf's Latin name is the first that we find recorded, for Isengrim was the central figure of the earliest stories. He owed his pre-eminence to a biblical saying which was the seed from which the beast epic grew. In Matthew VII, 15, Christ, concluding his sermon on the mount, told his hearers, 'Beware of false prophets, which come to you in sheep's clothing, but inwardly they are ravening wolves'. There the monks found a suggestion for the travesty by which they turned human society into a menagerie. They could have found it also, of course, in the fables of classical antiquity, and these certainly supplied part of the material from which the beast epic developed. But the fables alone cannot account for the prominence of the wolf in the early stages of its growth. The Flemish poet who wrote the Latin poem Isengrimus *in 1152 must have had that biblical passage in mind when he arranged the animal tales he had collected around the figure of the wolf.*

Two centuries before him another monk in the monastery of Toul in Lor-raine had composed a little beast epic which he entitled Ecbasis Captivi. *A calf escapes from the stable and falls into the clutches of the wolf. But the wolf receives his reward through a wile of the fox. The lion, king of all the beasts, has fallen sick and summons all his subjects before him, hoping to find one who can cure him. The fox is the only one who does not appear, and in his*

49

absence he is accused by the wolf of various crimes. When he finally obeys the summons he blames his belated arrival at court on his enemies: they failed to summon him three times as required by law. He then prescribes a cure for the lion, which proves effective. The patient is wrapped in the warm hide stripped off the wolf's back.

Here are features of the story that Willem told in his Flemish poem: the lion's court, the summoning of the fox, the mutilation of the wolf at the fox's suggestion. But the beasts are still anonymous abstractions of the ancient fables; they have not yet received a distinct individuality by being endowed with proper names. These seem to have come into literary use in the course of the twelfth century. To judge from Guibert's testimony they were not yet popular in his lifetime. They did not gain wider currency until secular poets, after 1150, began to tell wolf and fox stories in the vernacular. French poets took the lead. Their stories, called branches of the Roman de Renart—*a term employed by the poets themselves—are of unequal value, but the originator of the series was a man of talent, and was held in respect by his less gifted imitators, to whom we owe the preservation of his name. The author of a very late Tale, who wrote in the second quarter of the thirteenth century, still knew him as the pioneer, who had been the first to recount the adventures and affairs of Reynard:*

> Signor, oi aves asses
> Et ans et jors a ja passes
> Les aventures et le conte
> Que Pierre de Saint Cloot conte
> De Renart et de ses affaires.

And the author of the sixteenth branch, a mediocre product, could think of no better scheme to recommend his trifle to the public than by foisting it upon Pierre qui de Saint Clost fu nez.

There was also an early German version called Isengrînes Nôt *by Heinrich der Glîchezâre,* *of which only fragments have been preserved. It was*

* Glîchezâre *means 'sneak', and was, apparently, not Heinrich's nickname, but that of his hero, the fox. See* Zeitschrift für Deutsches Altertum, LXIII, *pp. 214–6.*

written in the early eighties of the twelfth century, and was elaborated by a later poet into the story of Reinhart Fuchs. But both French and German versions were surpassed by Willem's poem. The Fleming handled the borrowed material so deftly and with so much freedom and originality that the adaptation is universally conceded to be the best specimen of the genre in any language.

One manuscript of Willem's beast epic makes him say in the prologue that he continued the work of another man called Arnout, who had left Reynard's story uncompleted. The poem seems to bear the earmarks of dual authorship. It opens with a series of unconnected episodes which the narrator has skilfully strung together; but after line 1883 one episode absorbs all our attention: the trial of the wicked fox. The fun and the humour that prevail in the earlier part are less prominent in the trial scene. A shiver of suspense comes over the reader as soon as Reynard has given himself up. The story does not lose its comic implications, but the dominating mood is one of tense anxiety. That is the reason why some critics are inclined to believe that Willem was the continuator of a poem begun by Arnout and that he added a prologue after he had joined his own and Arnout's part into a well-knit whole.

But others are sceptical about Arnout's right to literary fame. The opening lines of Willem's prologue are closely patterned on those of Le Plaid. In this the French poet declares that he will remedy the neglect of a predecessor, a certain Perrot, who failed to recount the trial and judgement of Renart. Is not the Arnout of the Flemish epic, the sceptics ask, a Dutch substitute for Perrot? They assume, in other words, that Willem did not declare his intention to fill a gap left by a fellow poet and compatriot, but that he simply repeated in his own language what the poet of Le Plaid had said about Perrot.

I am inclined to side with the sceptics. One can easily imagine how the change from Perrot to Arnout came about. A copyist of the French text wrote .errot, leaving space open for the rubricator to fill in an ornamental capital P. The rubric was never inserted, and the Flemish poet into whose hands the manuscript passed made of the truncated name a good Flemish one that was almost similar to it. He did not care about the correct name of the neglectful poet, but since he had to be given a name, it should be one with which his Flemish readers were familiar. And in that way the Frenchman Perrot, who was no other than Pierre de Saint Cloud, was rechristened *Arnout* by his Flemish fellow poet.

If this is what actually happened, it does not follow, however, that the assumption of dual authorship is untenable. But it cannot be based on *Willem's* own testimony. The only evidence for it is the poem itself. Having scanned *Willem's* verse almost every day over a long period of time as the labour of translation slowly progressed, I remain unconvinced that it is the work of two poets. But this is the subjective opinion of a brother poet who can bring no other proof except the testimony of his ear and his artistic intuition. And that is worth little, I admit, when pitted against the objective arguments brought forward by painstaking philologists. But the matter is of slight importance. The play's the thing, not the question of authorship. And the play is a well-constructed comedy that has delighted successive generations of readers for more than six centuries.

The many imitations to which it gave rise are proof of its enduring popularity. It was translated into Latin verse by a contemporary of *Willem's*. An anonymous poet of the fourteenth century composed a sequel to it, expanding it to a poem of 7,794 lines, which goes by the name of Reynard's Story. The invention of printing gave it a renewed vogue. Reynard's Story was printed in 1487 by Gheraert Leeu at Antwerp. The text was reproduced fairly accurately, but a certain Henric van Alcmaer had divided it into chapters and inserted moralizing glosses. It was in this form that the story gained currency far beyond the borders of the Low Countries. For Henric van Alcmaer's text was translated into Middle Low German and printed at Lübeck in 1498, and this edition was again translated into High German, Danish, Swedish, English, Icelandic and Latin, and finally retold in hexameters by no less a poet than Goethe.

Willem's poem gave ample scope to a burlesque portrayal of human life and parodied with subtle humour the aristocratic romance of chivalry. Its literary satire eludes the modern reader, but its social implications are as clear and enjoyable today as they were to *Willem's* contemporaries. Reynard is a creator of high and low comedy. Impudence, mendacity, sly wit, flattery, sarcasm are the weapons on which he relies, and he knows intuitively which of these will serve him best in each situation. The poet had a sneaking love for

his foxy hero and felt no qualms of conscience in recounting his repeated es-
capes from the punishment which from an ethical point of view he fully de-
served. A strain of tragedy, however, runs through this highly comic story.
Reynard, the outlaw, is a lonely fellow. He is set upon by all the world, and
the only place where, as the story ends, he finds security for himself and his
family is a bleak wilderness that is shunned by all other beasts. The life he
leads is not of his own choosing. It is his destiny so to live. He must act the
villain's part that an inscrutable fate has assigned to him in the mystery play
of life, and his claim to pardon is that he plays it to perfection.

ADRIAAN J. BARNOUW

Willem, who laboured to indite*
Madoc in many a wakeful night,**
Willem took it much to heart
That one adventure of Reynard
5   In Dutch remained as yet untold,
Which had not been writ of by Arnold.
For that legend he made a search
And began to tell it in Dutch
After the French in which it was made.
10   May God grant me his aid!
Now I would with all my heart
Make a request at the start,
To every fool and country clown,
If they happen to come to town
15   And hear these rhymes read in Dutch,
Which will not benefit them much,
That from carping they refrain—
They're like the raven ever fain
To croak some impertinence.
20   They'll say—those verses make no sense—
Though they know of poetry nothing at all,
As little as I know what to call
The folk now living in Babylon.
'Twere well they left such things alone.
25   I say this not for my own sake.
I would not presume to make

---

* The verse is a faithful reproduction of the original. It has no iambic regularity but skips and dances with great freedom. Each line has four beats, but the number of light syllables varies between three and seven.

** Willem's poem 'Madoc' has not been preserved. Maerlant says in his 'Rijmbijbel': 'This is not Madoc's dream/Neither Reynard's nor Arthur's pranks'. That is doubtless an allusion to Willem's other poem, but unfortunately Maerlant tells us nothing about its contents.

A poem but for the request
Of one accustomed to invest
All that she does with courtesy.
30 She it was who persuaded me
To tell this adventure of Reynard.
Against carpers I'm on my guard,
Fools and bumpkins, the whole crew.
Rather would I be listened to
35 By such as observe etiquette
And have their minds ever set—
Rich or poor, whichever they be—
On behaving courteously.
Mark my words without fail.
40 Now listen how I begin my tale.
   It was on a day at Whitsuntide
That both wood and countryside
With green leaves were newly clad.
Noble, the king, it was who had
45 His court proclaimed everywhere,
Which he wanted to repair
To his glory, if he could.
There came to his court a multitude
Of beasts, great and small, in flocks,
50 Except alone Reynard, the fox.
Such wrong he had done against the court
That to it he durst not resort.
'Who doeth wrong, he feareth the light',
As clerks very truly write.
55 Even so did Reynard shun
The court where he was praised by none.
When the court had convened
There was no one but complained,
Except the badger, against Reynard,
60 The fierce one with the ruddy beard.

Great outcry thereupon began:
Isengrim and his clan
Came and stood before the king.
Isengrim began suing
65 And spoke, 'King, noble Sir,
By your glory and honneur,
In the name of mercy and right,
Do avenge the great despite
Which Reynard did to me,
70 From whom I did repeatedly
Suffer injury and grief.
Above all else I hold a brief
Against him for whoring my dame,
And also for a filthy shame
75 He did my children, whom he bepissed
So that two of them have missed
Ever since their eyesight.
But he did me further spite.
Things later came to such a pass
80 That a day agreed-on was
On which Reynard was to swear
His innocence. However, ere
The saints' images had been brought,
Reynard had a change of thought
85 And absconded to his fort.
Sire, the best who came to court
Today know this to be so.
Reynard, that wicked foe,
Has wronged me out and out.
90 Well I know, without doubt,
If all the cloth they make at Ghent
Were turned into parchment,
They could not write it all thereon.
Therefore I let it be gone.

95   Only my poor wife's disgrace
           Is a crime I can't dismiss
           Unrecorded and unrued.'
              After Isengrim had thus sued,
           Up stood a dog was called Cortois,
100   Who complained in French patois
           How one time he was so poor
           That he owned nothing more,
           In a cold winter frost,
           Than one sausage which he lost
105   Through Reynard's thievery.
              Tybert, the cat, angrily
           Jumped into the centre of the ring,
           And he spoke to Noble, the King,
           'Sire, since with Reynard you do not hold,
110   There is none here, young or old,
           But he has a charge to bring.
           And Cortois complains of a thing
           That happened many years ago.
           That sausage belonged to me, although
115   I don't complain. It was won
           In a mill where I had gone
           A-hunting. There, by a clever wile,
           One dark night, I stole it while
           The miller was sleeping heavily.
120   It is through no one else but me
           That Cortois can claim a part.
           This suit that Cortois would start
           Had much better be dismissed.'
           Pancer, the beaver, spoke, 'Is it
125   Right that this charge should be thrown out?
           Reynard is a murderous lout,
           And a trickster and a thief.
           He has no one so lief,

Not even my lord, the King,
130 But he would have him lose everything,
Life and honour, if he could gain
Thereby a fat morsel of a hen.
Who dare pretend this is hearsay?
Did he not only yesterday
135 Commit the greatest crime that e'er
Was done against Coward, the hare,
Who never wronged another beast?
For he, under the king's peace
And within the safety of the King,
140 Promised to teach him to sing
His creed and make him a chorister,
And made him sit without stir
In between both his legs.
Then they spelt and read the text
145 Of their creed and sang it aloud
As hard between them as they could.
It so happened that I got
To pass at the time that very spot.
There I heard them sing duet.
150 I went thither without let,
Making haste as I went.
There I found Reynard intent,
Not on teaching Coward sing
As he had begun doing,
155 But on playing his old game:
To throttle Coward was his aim,
And Coward's life would have been spent,
Had I not come, by accident,
That very moment to his aid.
160 Look, the wounds that he made
On poor Coward are still fresh.
Sire, King, I protest,

If you leave this crime unwroken
By which your peace is thus broken
165   And don't avenge it as your men ordain,
Your children still will bear the blame
Over many a year hence.'

    'By God, Pancer, you speak sense,'
Said Isengrim where he stood.
170   'Were Reynard dead, it would be good
For all of us, so help me God.
If Reynard should be spared the rod,
He'll cheat, before the month is full,
Many an unsuspecting fool.'

175   Grimbert, the badger, leapt up anon—
He was Reynard's brother's son—
And retorted in an angry tone,
'Sir Isengrim, it is well known
And an old proverb, forsooth,
180   "Enemy's mouth speaks seldom truth".
My uncle, you say, did you injury.
May that one hang upon a tree
By his throat as a thief
(Sir Isengrim, were it you lief,
185   I'd make a bet thereon with you)
Who did to others, of you two,
Greater harm, you or he.
My uncle is not here with me
As plaintiff, but had he at court
190   The king's favour and good report,
Sir Isengrim, as you have got,
Then the King would like it not,
And you would not escape rebuke
For that your sharp teeth often took
195   A bite out of my uncle's hide,
Which Reynard could not well abide.

I am not telling any lies.
Often and in many a wise
My poor uncle was made your fool.
200 Do you remember that wagon full
Of skate you were to throw from the car
To him, who followed after far,
And you took the whole fat lot
To stuff your guts with and gave him naught,
205 Neither a big nor a little one,
Except a skimpy fish's bone
Of which you did not like the taste?
That's all you gave him from that feast.
Some time later you had taken
210 A fat and tasty rasher of bacon
Which you put in your bag.
When Reynard claimed his part of the swag
You answered him in mockery,
"I will give it you readily,
215 Reynard, handsome chap and young.
The hook on which the bacon hung
Drips with fat; go gnaw thereon."
It was small profit Reynard won
When he got that goodly slab
220 At great peril; for one did grab
Reynard and threw him into his sack,
Out of which, by a clever knack,
He broke loose well-nigh dead.
That's the hazardous life he led
225 All through Isengrim's fault,
And twice as bad as I have told.
Don't you think, sirs, that's enough?
Yet there's even more brazen bluff
In his complaining about his wife,
230 Who has loved Reynard all her life

Just as he has loved her.
They did not make a land-wide stir
About it, though, but I dare swear
That for more than seven year
235   Reynard has possessed her troth.
And if Hersinde was nothing loath,
Out of love and courtesy,
To do his will, what of it? she,
The comely dame, was soon restored.
240   Why waste on that another word?
Now comes Sir Coward, the hare, and blows
A bubble up to a mighty cause.
Coward badly recited his creed!
Might not Reynard, who taught him to read,
245   Strike his pupil? If that were
Forbidden, by God, it wouldn't be fair.
Cortois complains that he lost
A sausage when there was a frost.
He had better withdraw that suit.
250   Don't you know it was stolen loot?
'*Male quesite, male perdite*', that means,
The gain that is got by evil means
By evil means is lost again.
Who would care to complain
255   If Reynard seized stolen ware?
None who knows foul from fair.
Reynard is a righteous man.
Since the king ordered his ban
To be proclaimed and his peace,
260   He never did anything amiss—
I know that well—so that you might
Take him for a hermit or anchorite.
Close to his skin he wears a hair.
He has not eaten all this year

265 Any meat, neither wild nor tame;
I was told so by those who yesterday came
From yonder. He left his castle Malcrois.
Rather than there, it is his choice
To make his lair in a hermit's cell.
270 He gets—as far as I can tell—
No other livelihood or fee
Than the alms he receives from charity.
He looks pale and pines away,
He suffers for his sins all day
275 Hunger, thirst, self-made pain.'
       When Grimbert, talking in this vein,
Reached this point, they became aware
That from the heights Sir Chanticleer
Was descending and coming near,
280 And he brought upon a bier
A dead hen, Coppe by name.
Reynard had killed this dame
By biting her in the crop, poor thing.
Chanticleer came to tell the King.
285 He strutted in front of the corpse
Beating his wings with much force.
To left and right of the stretcher came
A rooster; both of worldwide fame.
Cantart was called the one,
290 He who had for a godson
The noble cock of Dame Alent.
I believe that the other went
By the name of Cock Crayand,
The handsomest rooster in all the land
295 Between Poland and Portugal.
Each of them carried a tall
Burning candle, straight as a pole,
For their sister Coppe's soul,

For they were brothers of the lass.
300　　They were crying, 'Woe me, alas!'
They made a great outcry and moan
Because their sister Coppe was gone.
Pinte and Sprute carried the bier.
They were sad and without cheer
305　　Because their little sister had died.
One could hear far and wide
These two lamenting her sad fate.
Thus they entered the debate.
Chanticleer leapt into the ring
310　　And said, 'Sire, Lord King,
By God's mercy I beg of your Majesty,
Have pity on the injury
Which Reynard did to me and my dear
Children that are standing here
315　　Robbed of all pleasure and fun.
April had just begun
And the winter had gone out,
And one saw the flowers sprout
Everywhere in the green field.
320　　I was proud of my yield
Of children, quite a family.
Eight fine sons I had with me,
And seven daughters, finer still.
Being alive gave them a thrill.
325　　Roda, she who was a match
To the wisest, bore them in one hatch.
They were strong and stuffed with lard
And went about in a fine yard
That was all around fenced in.
330　　There was a large barn within,
Which was guarded by several dogs,
Who tore many beasts their togs.

Hence my children had no fear.
Reynard hated to see them here
335   Living in so secure a spot
That not one could be caught.
That vicious neighbour Reynard
Kept running around the yard
In hope of trapping one of my brood.
340   When the dogs spied him, they pursued
The miscreant with all their might.
Once they got him in a tight
Corner, on the edge of the moat.
There I saw him pay more than a groat
345   For his thefts and robberies,
So that the wool flew off his fleece.
Yet he got away by sleight.
God curse the wicked wight!
Then for a time he would behave,
350   Till he returned, the murderous knave,
Reynard, in a hermit's weed
And brought me a document to read,
A letter to which, I could see,
Your seal was set, your Majesty.
355   I began to peruse
This letter, and saw it brought the news
That you had royally ordained
Throughout the land over which you reigned
Peace to every living beast
360   And bird, the biggest and the least.
Other news he brought that morn.
He told me that he had forsworn
The world and was a hermit now
Doing heavy penance and how
365   He had kept a strict fast
For sins he committed in the past,

And had suffered many a hurt.
He showed me his pilgrim's staff and shirt,
Which he had brought from the Elmare,*
370 And under it a prickly hair.
Then he said, "Now you may,
Sir Chanticleer, live for aye
Without any fear of me.
By the stole I've sworn to be
375 Abstinent of meat and fat.
Besides, I'm getting old, so that
I must tend my soul from now on.
God be with you, I must be gone,
I have business I may not delay.
380 I still have the day's prayers to say
For midday, noon, and prime."
He left, without wasting time,
And at once began to read,
Going along a hedge, his creed.
385 I was glad and unafraid
And went where my children played,
So completely off my guard
That I took them, without regard
For safety, outside the fence.
390 There I met with mischance.
Reynard was lying in wait, the wretch.
He had crept through the hedge
And cut us off from the gate.
One of my brood became his bait.
395 It was snatched from the rest
And bagged by Reynard, that cursed pest.
Disaster was in store for me then.
For since he had the taste of a hen
In his gluttonous muzzle, neither guard

* A monastery in Flanders.

400 Nor watchdog could keep Reynard
From doing harm to my family.
Have pity on us, your Majesty.
He has ever since lain in wait,
Both by day and by night,
405 To snatch one of my children away.
Their number is far less today
Than it used to be before.
Of fifteen only four
Remain alive. That vicious fiend
410 Reynard, in his gluttony, cleaned
All but four of them away.
The dogs, only yesterday,
Snatched Coppe out of his snout.
Here she lies under this clout.
415 I bring this charge in agony.
Lord king, have pity on me.'
   The king, addressing Grimbert, said,
'Your uncle who turned hermit led
A life of penance so severe
420 That, if I live another year,
He'll know it. Listen, Sir Chanticleer,
I've heard enough and to spare.
Your daughter is dead. Here she lies.
God tend her soul in paradise.
425 We may not keep her with us, Sir.
We will let God take care of her,
And we shall sing our vigils here.
Then we shall carry her on the bier
To her burial place in state.
430 After that we shall debate
With these lords how we best
Can avenge on that pest
The foul murders he has done.'

Thus he spoke. And thereupon
435 He commanded young and old
To sing vigils. As they were told
By royal command they did at once.
They could be heard in consonance
Intoning very loud and slow
440 The *placebo domino*
And the verses belonging thereto.
Were it not too long to do,
I would tell you which of them
Intoned there the requiem,
445 And by whom the seventh lesson was read.
The vigils over, they put Coppe to bed
In a grave that had been made
With great skill in the shade
Of a linden among the grass.
450 A marble slab smooth like glass
Was the stone over her grave.
And the lettering on it gave
The reader passing by to know
Who lay buried there below.
455 These were the words that were writ
Upon the tombstone over the pit:
'Here Coppe was laid to rest
Who could scrape with the best,
Killed by Reynard, who ever has been
460 The cruel pursuer of her kin.'
Now Coppe lies under mould.
The king's counsellors, wise and old,
Were called to consider in what way
Reynard could be made to pay
465 For this heinous offence.
They told the king it was the sense
Of their meeting that he ought

To summon Reynard to court
And Reynard should not be allowed to use
470 His weal or woe as an excuse
For not appearing before the king,
And that the act of summoning
Should be entrusted to Bruin, the bear.
The king decided then and there
475 To send Bruin and spoke to him:
   'Sir Bruin, before this sanhedrim
I entrust this mission to you.
Be wise, I pray, in all you do.
Guard yourself against deceit.
480 Reynard is vicious and a cheat.
He will cajole you and lie.
With false words he will try
To mislead you and betray.
By God, he'll trick you, if he may.'
485   'My Lord, stop lecturing me,'
Said Bruin. 'I'll be damned if he
Play me foul, that vicious brat,
Without me giving him tit for tat,
That he won't know where to turn.
490 On my account have no concern.'
He takes his leave and goes his way
To where he will meet with foul play.
   Now Bruin has made a start.
He despises in his heart
495 The thought, which he considers mad,
That anyone should be so bad
As to make a fool of him.
Through a forest dark and dim
He came to a desert waste,
500 Across which Reynard had traced
Many a winding, crooked trail

When, out of the wooded dale,
He came running after prey.
On the edge of the desert lay
505 A mountain, a high and sprawling mass.
Bruin, the bear, had to pass
Over the top to make his way
To Maupertuis where Reynard lay.
Many houses Reynard possessed,
510 But of all these the best
Was the castle of Maupertuis.
Thither he went secretly
Whenever things with him went wrong.
   Now Bruin had gone so long
515 That he arrived at Maupertuis
And saw the gate through which usually
Reynard passed when he left and ran.
Bruin, in front of the barbican,
Sat on his tail and called out:
520 'Reynard, are you about?
I'm Bruin, the king's messenger.
By his God I heard him swear,
If you fail to come and report,
And I produce you not in court,
525 There to receive and give what is due,
He will take the life of you,
He will break you on a wheel.
Reynard, I tell you for your weal,
Come with me to the court.'
530   Reynard listened to this report
As he was lying within his gate,
Where he often used to wait
For the sun to grow less hot.
Hearing these words he doubted not
535 That the visitor was Bruin,

And he retreated deeper down
Into his darkest burrowings.
Manifold were his musings.
What ruse could he hit on
540 To make Bruin, that glutton,
The butt of laughter and put him to shame
And yet himself escape all blame?
    After a long while Reynard said:
'Thanks, your advice comes in good stead,
545 Sir Bruin, my dear old friend.
Whoever persuaded you to wend
All this long, weary way
Over the mountain, meant to play
A prank on you; he served you ill.
550 I would go to court by my free will,
Even without your good rede,
But I happened, alas, to feed
My belly on more than enough
Of a queer, new-fangled stuff,
555 So that I fear I cannot go,
Sitting and standing hurt me so.
I am so terribly overfed.'
    'What was it you ate?'—Reynard said:
'Nothing, Bruin, of any account.
560 A poor man is not a count.
You can tell that by me.
We poor folk must eat, you see,
What we would scorn if we could choose.
Good fresh honeycombs that ooze
565 Abundance of honey were my feed.
Those I must swallow out of need,
When nothing better can be had.
But eating them makes me sad
With discomfort and pain.'

570   Hearing this, Bruin spoke again:
'Reynard, by the day of doom,
You care that little for honey in the comb?
Honey is such a sweet food,
I know no other that is so good.
575 To me it is the daintiest bit.
Reynard, get me some of it.
Dear cousin, noble Reynard,
I shall love you with all my heart
As long as I live, if you do,
580 And I may get some honey through you.'
'Get you honey, Bruin? you're tricking me.'
'I'm not, Reynard, I could not be
So mad as to make a fool of you.'
Said Reynard, 'You want some, you really do?
585 If you want honey for a mess,
Let me know in all seriousness.
If you do, you can eat your fill.
I'll get you so much, ten of you will
Not be able to eat it all,
590 If that would give me the right to call
On you for help.' 'What, ten of us?
Reynard, you're not serious.
You can surely count on this:
Had I all the honey that now is
595 Between here and Portugal,
In one meal I'd eat it all.'
    Reynard replied, 'You don't say!
A villager, Lamfret, lives close by.
You couldn't in seven years or more
600 Eat all the honey he has in store.
I would deliver that into your paws,
Sir Bruin, if you will back my cause
And plead on my behalf at court.'

Bruin promised him his support
605 And swore if Reynard gave him his fill
Of honeycombs (of which he will
Scarcely get a bite at all)
He would be, whatever befall,
His good companion and faithful friend.
610 Reynard chuckled at that no end,
And spoke, 'Bruin, famous thane,
I wish God would let me gain
Such a windfall as for thee
This honey promises to be,
615 Though seven barrels were thy wish.'
Those words sounded heavenish
To Bruin and did his heart good.
He laughed as he never more would.
Reynard thought, standing there,
620 'Bruin, if fortune plays me fair,
I shall yet leave you there today
Where your laughter will be less gay.'
Thinking thus, Reynard stepped out
And hailed Bruin with a shout:
625 'Uncle Bruin, welcome, dear friend.
If you would attain your end
We must not tarry here all day.
Follow me, I'll show the way.
We shall take this winding trail.
630 You'll get your fill without fail.
If all goes as I hope it may
You will surely yet today
Get as much as you can bear.'
Reynard meant, a generous share
635 Of blows; that's what he promised him.
But Bruin's mind was too dim
To see what Reynard was hinting at,

Who taught him to steal honey that
Was to cost him all too dear.
640   Reynard, conversing with his compeer
Bruin, arrived at Lamfret's place
And went inside the enclosed space.
    Shall I tell you what sort of man
Lamfret was? If I can
645   Rely on hearsay, a carpenter, good
At his craft. Out of the wood
He had brought an oak tree into his yard
To split in two. He had worked hard
To jam two wedges into the split.
650   Carpenters are still doing it.
These kept the trunk gaping wide,
To Reynard's joy, for it would provide
The means he needed to his end.
He laughed and said, 'Sir Bruin, dear friend,
655   Search and look carefully.
Here inside this very tree
Is plenty of honey to make you gloat.
Try to get it down your throat
And into your belly if you can.
660   But practice self-control, dear man.
However good the honey taste,
Eat not to excess, nor in haste,
Lest you perish in the quest.
I'd be dishonoured and dispossessed,
665   Came you to grief, Uncle dear.'
    Bruin spoke, 'Reynard, have no fear.
Do I seem a fool to you?
Measure is good in all you do.'
Reynard spoke, 'That's truly said.
670   Foolish of me to be afraid.
Go to at once and creep in.'

Bruin thought of what he would gain
And, fooled by the promise of the bait,
Thrust his forepaws and his pate
675   Over the ears into the split.
Reynard, putting all his strength to it,
Pulled the wedges out of the tree.
Bruin, who had used such flattery,
Was caught in the oak and could not budge.
680   Nephew, by a crafty dodge,
Has now got Uncle in such a fix
That neither by strength nor cunning tricks
He can escape at any price,
His head being held as in a vice.
685   What would you now counsel Bruin to do?
He is strong and brave, it is true,
But that won't help him out of the snare.
Reynard had fooled him, he was aware.
Bruin began to roar and shout.
690   He was caught by his snout
And both his forepaws so tight
That his efforts availed him not a mite.
He despaired of ever making good
His escape. Reynard, from where he stood
695   At a distance, watched and espied
Lamfret, the carpenter, who hied
Homeward with a hatchet and a sharp axe.
Now you may hear how Reynard, the fox,
Began to mock Bruin, the bear:
700   'Uncle Bruin, tuck in the fare!
Here comes Lamfret to fill your cup.
After eating, you ought to sup.'
        Having spoken those words Reynard strolled
Back again to his stronghold,
705   Without a goodbye. And just then

The bear came into Lamfret's ken,
Who saw at once that he was caught.
He didn't remain nailed to the spot.
He went for help at a running pace
710 Where it could be had in the nearest place,
Down in the village near by.
He raised among neighbours a hue and cry:
'A bear is trapped in my yard!'
There followed him a mighty guard.
715 In the village remained not a living soul.
All ran who could run at all,
In order to bring the bear to his doom.
One in the crowd carried a broom,
Another a flail, another a rake,
720 This one came running with a stake,
Each as he came away from work.
Even the parish priest wouldn't shirk
His duty, but brought his cross for the kill
Which the verger yielded against his will.
725 And even the verger carried a banner
Wherewith to poke and to hammer.
Dame Julock, the priest's better half,
Came running with her distaff,
Around which she had wound her wool that day.
730 Many a slut who for decay
And age had hardly a tooth at best
Came hopping along with the rest.
Let him who cares beware of this:
He for whom things have gone amiss,
735 Who suffers grief or has a great fall,
Becomes the butt of one and all.
Poor man Bruin found that out.
Now he was threatened by many a lout
Who had not dared utter a sound

740 Had Bruin been free to paw around.
     He saw southward under the sun
     Lamfret armed with a hatchet run
     At the head of all the rabble.
     Although Bruin was in great trouble,
745 He foresaw greater yet
     And put all on one bet.
     When he heard the noise they made
     He wriggled and pulled till he flayed
     All the skin off his snout.
750 Though Bruin got his head out,
     With great labour and painful moan,
     Yet he left there of his own
     Both cheeks and one ear at least.
     One never saw an uglier beast.
755 How could he have met with worse mishap?
     He got his head out of the trap
     But could not manage to free his paws
     Without leaving behind the claws
     And both his gloves, a rough pair.
760 In pain he got away from there.
     How could he have been dishonoured more?
     Both his forepaws felt so sore
     That walking on them made him writhe.
     The blood ran down over his eyes
765 So that he was scarcely able to see.
     He dared not stay and could not flee.
     One, called Otram Longlob,
     Carried a club with a horny knob
     And kept poking at his eye.
770 Foul Martha stirred sharp lye
     For Bruin with a pikestaff.
     Abel Quack and Mistress Baff
     Were sprawling in the mire and fought

For a long pole they had brought.
775 Ludolf Long-Nose, carrying
A leaden whopper in a sling,
Started to swing it roundabout.
Long-fingered Seigneur Bertout
Blew in that band the first horn,
780 For he was the highest born,
Except only Lamfret.
Bandy-legged Hewlet
Was his father, that's well known.
Abstal was his native home,
785 And he a son of Dame Ogood,
Who patched up lantern frames of wood.
Many another woman and man,
More than I can mention, ran
To pound at Bruin and cause him pain,
790 So that he bled from every vein.
Bruin, the bear, the wretchedest
Of all creatures, was thus pressed
On an embankment by many a lout.
Pourparlers were ruled out.
795 One pounded, another bombarded him.
Lamfret attacked with the fiercest vim.
They caused great torment to the bear.
He sat and looked here and there
And took all that he was given.
800 He got the church's cross driven
Into his neck by the parish priest,
And the verger, not to be least,
Came poking at Bruin with the banner.
Lamfret proceeded in the grand manner:
805 With a sharp axe he let go
And struck at the nape of his neck a blow
That caused Bruin to stagger and sway.

The impact made him jump away
Between the river and hedgerow
810 Right in the midst of a dozen or so
Of old women, of whom he threw
A number of four or five into
The river that ran through that countryside
And which was very deep and wide.
815 The priest's wife was one of these.
Hence the priest felt little at ease,
When he saw her almost drowned.
He had no desire any more to pound
And poke at Bruin, but called to his flock,
820 'Brave parishioners, Dame Julock
Is floating yonder in the brook
With both her spindle and distaff. Look!
Go to and help her, all who may!
I give them for a year and a day
825 Full pardon and full remission too
Of every sin they may do!'
    Both men and women ran,
Leaving Bruin, that wretched man,
Lying there as good as dead.
830 They went to work where the priest said
With rope and pothook and shout.
While they were pulling the woman out,
Bruin plunged in and swam away
Quickly, to escape the fray.
835 Anger seized the village throng
When they saw Bruin swimming along
Where he could not be pursued.
On the river bank they stood
And hurled taunting words at him.
840 Bruin swam down the stream
Where the current was most strong

79

And prayed God to avenge his wrong
On that cursed oak tree
In which he left as a penalty
845 Cheeks and ears. And then he hissed
Curses upon that evil beast,
Faithless Reynard, the fox, who steered
His Uncle Bruin's brown beard
So deep into the oak tree,
850 Where Lamfret found him in agony
And made him suffer worse yet.
 Praying and cursing thus he let
The current carry him for a while,
Till he had floated half a mile
855 From the spot in the river's bend
Where the villagers remained.
He was spent with pain and tired.
Through loss of blood he nearly expired.
He was not on a pleasure jaunt.
860 He swam ashore and crawled to a haunt
Upon the bank where he could rest.
He was the saddest and wretchedest
Of beasts you ever set eyes upon.
He lay and groaned woe-begone,
865 And with his loins beat the bank.
For this he had Reynard to thank.
 Hear what Reynard did then:
He had caught a fat hen
On the heath by Lamfret's fence
870 Ere he had departed thence,
And had carried it up a hill
Far away from every trail,
Where not a creature was around.
It suited Reynard to the ground
875 That not a soul came that way,

So that he could dispose of his prey
Without any hinder or let.
When he had tucked that dainty bit
With feather and all into his belly
880 He went down into the valley
Along a well-hidden trail.
He had eaten his fill.
The weather was beautiful and hot.
He had run at so fast a trot
885 That the sweat ran down his cheek.
That's why he longed for the creek
Where he could make himself cool.
Reynard's heart, meanwhile, was full
Of manifold joyousness.
890 Lamfret, he thought, had doubtless
Dealt the deathblow to the wretch
And skinned him by the water's edge.
Luck has been with me, Reynard thought.
He who would harm me most at court
895 Has met his death through me today
Yet no one will be able to lay
The blame on me for his fate.
I have reason to celebrate.
   While Reynard was in this mood,
900 He looked down from where he stood
And saw Bruin lying below.
At the sight of his foe
Reynard was distressed and pained.
Where before joy had reigned,
905 There was now grief and scorn.
'Cursed be the day when you were born,
Lamfret,' Reynard swore.
'You are duller than a boar.
Lamfret, you son of a bitch,

910   You don't feel honour's itch.
How did you let this bear get free,
Whom you got in the trap through me?
Such a good morsel is thereon,
That many a man would feast upon.
915   O Lamfret, craven whoreson,
Upon the same day you won
And at once lost again
A most precious bear skin.'
    That was enough abuse this time,
920   Reynard thought, and started to climb
Downward to look at Bruin's plight.
He was indeed a bloody sight,
And miserably sick, and sore
With the many wounds he bore.
925   Reynard saw this with glee
And railed at him in mockery:
"Reverend priest, *Dieu vous garde.*
Would you like to see Reynard,
The red rogue, the beast of prey,
930   The knave? Well, here you may.
Now tell me, priest, dear friend,
By him you serve, do you intend
To enter a holy brotherhood,
Since you wear a scarlet hood?
935   Are you an abbot, or a prior?
Who tonsured you? I can't admire
The close shave he gave your ear.
You have lost your top clear
And taken off your gloves, I see.
940   You're going to sing, it seems to me,
The last service of the day.'
    Bruin listened in dismay.
What could he do? Punish the knave?

He had to let him rant and rave,
945 And took to the river as before.
He did not want evermore
To hear the rogue's impertinence.
He let himself be carried thence
Downward on the river's tide,
950 Till he reached the other side
At the nearest place to land,
And lay down upon the sand.
    How shall Bruin go to court?
Though all the world gave him support,
955 He could not walk on his paws.
The oak in which he lost his claws
A while ago, with the skin
Of both his forefeet, had been
So cruel a vice, it hurt him still.
960 He did not know, feeling so ill,
How he best could reach the king.
This was his manner of travelling:
He sat down on his arse
And performed the shameful farce
965 Of shoving forward over his tail.
And when that motion made him quail,
He would roll himself along.
He kept that up for a furlong,
Until he came to the king.
970 When they saw him tumbling
From afar in this style,
Many wondered for a while
What this rolling thing might be.
The king was among the first to see
975 What it was, and spoke at once,
'This is one of my adjutants.
It's Bruin, and see how red his head!

He is wounded and almost dead.
God, who maltreated him so?'
980 Meanwhile Bruin approached to show
His wounds to the king and complain.
He groaned and sighed time and again
And spoke as plaintiff: 'Your Majesty,
By your honour, avenge me
985 On Reynard, that vicious beast,
Who made me lose my handsome cheeks
With his old craftiness
And my left ear no less,
And has made me as you see.'
990 The king said, 'Verily,
I be damned if I do not.'
And then the king, on the spot,
Called his high barons by name
And commanded that they came
995 Jointly to his council board
To advise him in accord
How, to the king's honour, this crime
Should be punished. Most of them
Counselled that Reynard be summoned anew,
1000 If it pleased the king to listen to
The parties' plea and counterplea.
They also said they wished to see
Tybert, the tomcat, fare
With the summons to Reynard's lair.
1005 Though he was feeble, he was wise.
    The king approved of this advice.
'Go, Sir Tybert,' said the king,
'And don't return unless you bring
Reynard with you to the court.
1010 Some of these lords report
That Reynard, whatever he do

To other beasts, has faith in you
And gladly does what you say.
If he doesn't appear, I'll make him pay.
1015   I'll have him summoned once again
To the damage of all his kin.
Go, Tybert, tell him that.'
        'Sire, I am only a little cat,
A poor creature,' Tybert said.
1020   'Sir Bruin, who is strong and hot of head,
Couldn't make Reynard come and plead.
How then shall I succeed?'
        'Sir Tybert,' said the king,
'You have wisdom and learning.
1025   You are not big, that is true,
But many can with cunning do,
And with caution, of course,
What they could not do by force.
Go at once, do as I say.'
1030   Tybert spoke, 'God I pray
That He speed me where I go.
I am off on a journey, though,
That makes me downcast of mood.
God give me nothing but good.'
1035   Now must Tybert go his way.
He is afraid and far from gay.
He took the road and saw at once,
Flying in the far distance,
Saint Martin's own bird.
1040   Tybert rejoiced and was heard
Exclaiming, 'Hail, noble bard,
Turn your wing hitherward
And fly on my right side.'
The bird flew where he espied
1045   A wood in which he meant to land

And flew on Tybert's left hand.
This omen that he met did not
Spell much good, Tybert thought.
Had he seen the bird's flight
1050 Pass him by on his right
He would have thought it a good sign.
Now he felt his hope decline.
He did as others in such a case
And gave himself a bolder face
1055 Than his heart was inside.
He walked with a firm stride
Until he came to Maupertuis.

    Reynard, haughty as could be,
Was standing alone at his gate.
1060 Tybert spoke, it being late,
'Reynard, good evening.
The King threatens to have you swing
If you don't come to court with me.'
'Tybert, I bid you welcome be,
1065 Brave cousin of mine,' said Reynard.
'I recommend you in God's regard.
By God, I wish you all delight.'
Fine words cost Reynard not a mite.
Although his tongue spoke very well,
1070 His heart within was false and fell.
That will be shown in short time
Before you will have read this rhyme
About these two unto the end.

    'Cousin,' said Reynard, 'my dear friend,
1075 Tonight you shall stay with me.
Come in, and tomorrow early
We shall together go to court.
Among my kin of every sort
There's no one, Tybert, whom I dare

1080 Trust so well as you, I swear.
Bruin, the glutton, came to my place.
He showed me such a fierce face
And looked to me so strong of limb
That I wouldn't have gone with him,
1085 Not for a thousand mark, I swear.
But, cousin, with you I'll gladly fare
To court tomorrow at break of day.'
Tybert said, 'I'd rather not stay.
Much better, if you ask me,
1090 To go to court immediately
Than to wait all night until
Morning. The moon shines on the hill
Just as clear as the day.
Never was seen, I would say,
1095 A better time for us to go.'
'No, dear cousin, that is not so.
I know some people who will greet
You and me whenever we meet
By day, but who won't treat us right
1100 If we happen to meet them by night.
You must stay tonight with me.'
    Tybert answered, 'What should we
Sup on if I stayed with you?'
Said Reynard, 'Dear cousin, it is true,
1105 The food is wretched here just now.
I can give you, if you allow,
A honeycomb, which is a good
And easily digested food.
Would you like a piece of it?'
1110   Tybert said, 'Not a bit.
Have you nothing else in the house?
If you gave me a fat mouse,
That would be a real treat.'

'A fat mouse?' said Reynard. 'Sweet
1115 Cousin of mine, I tell you what;
A priest lives near this spot.
There is a barn built on to his house,
And therein is so many a mouse,
You could not carry them in a wain.
1120 I've often heard the priest complain
That they drive him out of door.'
'Fat mice? Reynard? I implore
God to let me get inside!'
'Do you mean it?' Reynard replied,
1125 'You like mice?' 'How could I not?
Reynard, don't talk such rot.
I'd rather eat mice than the finest paste.
Don't you know that mice taste
Better than any venison?
1130 Please do me a favour! run
With me to where those mice breed,
And I shall serve you in your need
As a true vassal, though you had been
The murderer of all my kin.'
1135 Reynard said, 'Are you fooling me?'
'No, Reynard, I mean it, seriously.'
'God knows, Tybert, were I sure of that,
You'd eat your fill this evening yet.'
'My fill, Reynard? How you brag!'
1140 'Tybert, Tybert, you are a wag.'
'I am in earnest, I swear to that.
Had I a mouse, one that is fat,
I would not sell it for a dime.'
'Follow me then, we mustn't lose time.
1145 Tybert, I will take you straight
To the place where you shall sate
Your hunger ere I part from you.'

'If you please, Reynard, do.
I'd follow you, were it to Mompelier.'
1150 'Go we then; we are tarrying here
All too long,' Reynard said.
    So the two went ahead
And ran to the place they wanted to gain
Without ever drawing rein,
1155 Till they reached the priest's barnyard.
The entrance to the place was barred
On all sides by an earthen wall.
Reynard had paid there a call
By breaking through the previous night,
1160 When he had clogged his appetite
With a rooster he stole from the priest.
Martin, his son, had never ceased
Raging after that mishap,
And he had fixed up a trap
1165 In front of the hole to catch the fox,
So eager was he to avenge the cock's
Murder. This Reynard knew.
He said to Tybert, 'Cousin, go to,
Here is the hole, in you go,
1170 And don't be deliberate and slow.
Set about you, catch them quick.
Listen how those mice squeak!
Come out again when you are full.
I shall stay in front of the hole
1175 And be waiting for you out here.
We two mustn't part till day appear,
When together we go to court.
What are you waiting for? make it short.
Go eat, and let us go back
1180 To my place; there'll be no lack
Of good cheer from my dame.'

'Shall I go through? All the same,
Reynard, is it safe, you believe?
A priest has tricks up his sleeve.
1185   I couldn't stand being snared.'
'Fie, Tybert, you were never afeared.
How makes fear you thus inept?'
    Tybert was ashamed and leapt
Where he met with great mishap.
1190   For ere he knew it he felt the trap
Close around his neck and chest.
Thus did Reynard cheat his guest.
    Tybert cowered, being aware
That he was caught in a snare.
1195   He leapt forward and—tightened the loop!
Then Tybert started to whoop
And betrayed himself in his need.
He made an outcry so great, indeed,
In the throes of despair,
1200   That Reynard, who was standing there
Out in the street, heard him yell.
He called out, 'Do they taste well,
Tybert? Are they nice and fat?
If Martin knew that you sat
1205   Here at table and feasted upon
This dainty dish of venison
(How you digest it I don't know),
He would make you a sauce would go
Well with it; he's a courteous boy.
1210   While you are eating you sing for joy.
Tybert, is that the fashion at court?
I wish to God, who can do aught,
That Isengrim were with you there,
That vicious thief, that murderer,
1215   In such joy as you are in.'

Thus did Reynard chuckle and grin
Over Tybert's agony.
Tybert yelled heartrendingly,
So loud, that Martin, the priest's boy,
1220 Started up and cried for joy,
'Thank God, the trap was set
In time! For I have caught, I bet,
The chicken thief in my snare.
We'll make him pay for our Chanticleer.'
1225 With that he ran to the fireside
To light a torch of straw, and hied
To rouse his parents out of sleep
And all the children in a heap,
Crying, 'Go to, the thief is caught!'
1230 Soon you could see all the lot
Who were in the house running around.
Even the priest was seen to bound
Mother-naked from his cot.
Martin, in the meantime, got
1235 To Tybert and cried, 'I have him here!'
The parish priest managed to clear
The fire and seized his wife's distaff.
Dame Julock, in a great huff,
Took an offertory candle.
1240 The priest ran and started to handle
Tybert with the distaff.
Tybert had no cause to laugh,
Being beaten with a mighty din.
The priest stood in his naked skin
1245 And with his blows put the heat
On Tybert lying at his feet.
None of them left him alone.
The boy Martin seized a stone
And battered out one of his eyes.

1250   The priest, in the garb of paradise,
Raised his arm ready to strike.
When Tybert saw that he was like
To die anyway, then and there,
He felt the courage of despair
1255   And put the parish priest to shame.
With both his teeth and claws he came
Back at the priest for a surprise.
He leapt straight between his thighs
And pulled out that one thing
1260   That hung there merrily dangling
Within the stitchless satchel
With which a man rings the bell.
The thing fell down upon the floor.
The wife was furious and swore
1265   By her dead father's soul
She would gladly lose the whole
Of a year's offertory,
Could she have spared the priest this sorry
Mishap that put him to shame.
1270   She said, 'In cursed Satan's name
Must this snare have been set.
Come and look, Martin, my pet,
This was part of your father's trim.
It's loss for me and shame for him,
1275   For ever after everywhere.
Though he recover from the tear,
For the sweet game he'll be unfit.'
    Reynard, who heard her saying it,
Being still at the hole where he stood before,
1280   Laughed so that his backside tore
And his tavern started to creak.
In mockery he began to speak,
'Be silent, Julock, gentle dame.

Calm your grief, in God's name,
And refrain from such lament.
Though of his bells one is spent,
What of it? So much the less
Need he toil in pain and stress.
Why should you thus carry on?
If he recover, no harm is done.
The priest can toll with one bell.'
Thus sought Reynard to dispel
Dame Julock's sore distress.
The priest was losing consciousness,
Tottered, and fell in a faint.
The woman lifted him up and strained
Her muscles to carry him straight to bed.
    Reynard, in the meantime, sped
Back to his lodging all alone,
Leaving Tybert on his own,
In great fear of impending death.
He felt, indeed, at his last breath.
But when he saw them all in a scare
About the priest, who was lying there
Wounded, Tybert with the last of his grit
Set his teeth to work and bit
The snare in two. When he was free
He would not stay but made to flee.
He cleared the hole that let him through
And reached the road, which took him to
The king's court, ever straight on.
Before he arrived there it was dawn,
And the sun began to rise.
He entered in a poor man's guise
Into the court, Tybert did,
Who at the priest's had coveted
And won what he long will rue.

The king, at sight of Tybert, flew
In a rage, because the cat had lost
1320 One of his eyes, and angrily tossed
Terrible threats at the knave Reynard.
The king at once, without retard,
Called on his barons for advice.
How, he asked, could he best chastise
1325 Reynard for his wickedness?
Many plans for getting redress
From Reynard for his insolence
Were proposed in the conference.
Grimbert, the badger, submitted one.
1330 He was Reynard's brother's son.
'Lords,' he spoke, 'much counsel you had.
But were my uncle ever so bad,
We must keep the law at any price.
Reynard must be summoned thrice,
1335 As one does a freeborn man.
If he defies us, then we can
Declare him guilty of everything
For which, in the hearing of the king,
These lords here indicted him.'
1340 'Who should be the summoner, Grim?'
The king asked. 'Is any one here
Willing to put an eye or ear
In jeopardy, just for the sake
Of a felon? None would take
1345 The risk to be that foolish, I guess.'
Grimbert spoke, 'Before God I confess,
As you see me here, I am so brave.
With your permission, Sire, I crave
The charge of taking the summons to him.'
1350 'Go then, Grimbert, follow your whim.
But be wary and on your guard.'

'I shall, Sire, I know Reynard.'
Thus Grimbert goes to Reynard's den.
When he arrived he found him in
1355 With his wife Hermeline
And the whelps of his line,
Lying in a dugout.
Grimbert, the badger, made a stout
Entrance and greeted his uncle and aunt.
1360 'I wonder,' he said, 'that you can't
Resent the bad report you're in.
Don't you think it's time to begin
Your journey, in my company,
To the court of his Majesty,
1365 Where you are charged with many crimes?
You've now been summoned three times.
Don't fail tomorrow to appear,
For, I swear, it will cost you dear.
You can't expect mercy then.
1370 Three days later you'll see your den
And castle Maupertuis attacked.
In front of it they will erect
A gallows or a rack. I swear,
It is the truth that I declare.
1375 Both your children and your wife
Will be doomed to forfeit life
Shamefully, the king swore,
And you're, of course, past praying for.
Therefore, you had better go
1380 To court with me. Do not say no.
You never can tell what is to be.
Stranger adventure has frequently
Befallen you on one day
Than the chance of your coming away
1385 From court, tomorrow, with the king

His leave, amid all gathering.'
    Reynard said, 'That is true.
However, when the King's retinue
That I shall find there in his court
1390 Sees me enter, it would be short
Of a miracle if I came away.
They are all set on making me pay.
And yet, it would be better, I think,
Nom atter whether I float or sink,
1395 To go to court in your company
Than to put all in jeopardy:
Castle, children and my wife,
Not to mention my own life.
I cannot escape the king's power.
1400 Agreed? Then go we this very hour.
Listen,' he said, 'Dame Hermeline,
Watch over these kids of mine.
I recommend them to your care,
Above all others my son and heir
1405 My dear little Reynardine.
His tiny whiskers look so fine
Around his snout. I shall be glad
If he takes after his dad.
And here's that precious scamp Rossell.
1410 I love that boy just as well
As any one loved his brood.
Hermeline, if you are good
To my children, and God should grant
That I escape, I swear I shan't
1415 Be slow in rewarding you.'
    With courteous words he said adieu
In taking leave from his own,
Stepped outside, and was gone.
    Dame Hermeline stayed behind

1420	With her whelps, sad in mind,
	After she had seen Reynard
	Leave thus his house and yard
	Undefended as it stood.
	Now hear what mischief Reynard brewed.
1425	On reaching the moor where the heather grows
	He spoke to Grimbert, with a contrite pose,
	'Grimbert, look, nephew dear,
	How I sigh and quake with fear.
	Dread of death is now my fate.
1430	My remorse is so great
	For the sins that I have done.
	Dear nephew, my brother's son,
	Hear my shrift, I want it out!
	No other priest is here about.
1435	If you will only let me say
	My confession, then come what may,
	My soul shall be the more at ease!'
	Grimbert replied to this,
	'If you want to be shriven, Sir,
1440	Then you must at once forswear
	All theft and robbery,
	Or it will help you not a pea.'
	'Well I know it,' Reynard replied.
	'Grimbert, listen here by my side
1445	And give me counsel if you can.
	Look, I come as a penitent man
	To confess each wicked sin.
	Now listen, nephew, how I begin:
	Confiteor tibi, pater noster,
1450	That I wronged the cat and the rooster
	And treated all the animals ill.
	For that I'll atone, I swear I will.'
	'Uncle,' said Grimbert, 'no parleyvoo.

Speak to me, I beg of you,
1455 In language that I comprehend.'
　　Then said Reynard, 'I did offend
Against all beasts that live.
Pray to God that he forgive.
I got old Bruin in a pitiful state
1460 By giving him a bloody pate.
I showed Tybert where to catch mice
And had him caught as in a vice
At the priest's and beaten cruelly.
I also caused great misery
1465 To Chanticleer and his brood.
Little or big, they were all good
To eat, and many I took away.
No wonder he wants to make me pay.
Even the king went not scot-free.
1470 Him too I offered injury,
And so much insult to the queen
That she will hardly ever glean
Honour from me in like amount.
I also have, I must recount,
1475 Cheated Isengrim far worse
Than I could possibly rehearse.
My calling him uncle was a slip.
There is not any relationship.
I made him a monk at the Elmare,
1480 When we were in retreat there.
He never found a worse retreat!
I made him bind both his feet
On to the bell rope. He would like the din,
He thought, of tolling the tocsin,
1485 That he would learn it at any cost.
But the result was honour lost.
For he tolled much too loud,

So that down in the street the crowd
And all who were inside the Elmare
1490 Thought it was Satan and ran in a scare
To where they heard the bell being tolled.
The mob had nearly beaten him cold
Before he had time to speak and say,
"I want to become a monk and pray."
1495 Later I gave him a shaven crown.
He will never live that down,
In a long lifetime, I dare swear.
I made him burn off the hair
Till the skin began to shrivel.
1500 And yet, I cooked him greater evil
Teaching him fishing on the ice,
Where he was caught as in a vice
And given many a cruel blow.
Another day I made him go
1505 To the priest's with me in Bolois.
In all that region of Vermandois
There did not live so rich a priest.
That cleric had a larder, at least,
Where lots of fat bacon lay.
1510 I often carried some away.
In the floor of that larder I had made
A hole. It was easy to persuade
Isengrim to creep through that.
He found there beef in a vat
1515 And plenty of bacon on the hook.
Of that meat the glutton took
An immoderate quantity.
When he would beat it quietly
By the hole through which he came,
1520 His foul belly was not the same.
He had reason to curse his haul.

Where he had entered hungry and small
He couldn't get out full and fat.
I ran and gave the alarm. At that
1525   The village turned into a rout.
Listen how I brought that about.
I ran to where the priest sat
At his midday meal and ate.
A fat capon the priest possessed,
1530   Of all fowl the very best
That could be found in that land,
And so tame, it ate out of his hand.
I seized that capon where it stood
Before the table and fled pursued
1535   By the priest who cried, "Catch and kill!
You never saw and never will
See such a wonder! That thievish fox
Comes and steals one of my cocks
Within my house as I look on.
1540   By the Holy Ghost, a curse upon
The knave; he'll pay for it with his life!"
He seized the big table knife
And struck the board till it bent.
Then he lifted the table and sent
1545   It flying midway across the floor.
He cursed horribly and swore
At the top of his voice, "Catch and kill!"
I ran, and he upon my trail,
Swaying his knife in the chase.
1550   He followed me unto the place
Where Isengrim imprisoned was.
There I dropt the capon, because
It was too heavy a load for me
To carry between my teeth, you see,
1555   Though I was sorry to let it go.

Then cried the parish priest, "Oho!
Robber, you have to drop your theft."
I let him yell his loudest and left
To go where I wanted to be.
1560   The parish priest happened to see
Isengrim as he picked up his fowl.
Then the wolf had reason to howl.
The priest stabbed his eye with a knife.
Then six others joined the strife,
1565   Each armed with a large stave.
Seeing Isengrim, they gave
A loud yell, whereupon
The neighbours came running on
And spread the rumour all around
1560   That the parish priest had found
A wolf caught in his larder
By the belly, who couldn't get farther
Out of the hole that let him in.
The neighbours ran with kith and kin
1575   To look at this miraculous sight.
They struck Isengrim left and right
So that he had but little fun.
For the people made him run
The gauntlet of heavy blows and throws.
1580   In that way the villagers chose
To bandage Isengrim his eyes.
He could not stop them in any wise.
How they cudgelled Isengrim,
When they extricated him,
1585   Into a bruised battered wreck!
They tied a stone on to his neck,
And thus burdened let him go!
Then they cried, "Tally—ho!"
And set the dogs on Isengrim,

1590	But at the same time cudgelled him
	Till he was almost brought to bay.
	He fell upon the grass and lay
	Dead as stone, thought everyone.
	Then the children had great fun.
1595	This was something to talk about.
	On the bier they laid him out
	And carried him with great hullabaloo
	Through bushes and over stones into
	A ditch outside the village edge.
1600	He lay there all night among the sedge.
	I don't know how he came away.
	Then I got him to swear, some later day,
	Allegiance to me, a year ago.
	He swore it on condition, though,
1605	That I supply him with chickens galore.
	So I conducted him to the door
	Of a large house. Behind that,
	I gave him to understand, there sat
	A dozen hens and a rooster, high
1610	Under the rafter and close by
	A trapdoor. Isengrim
	At my prompting, and I with him,
	Climbed to the roof, thatched with straw.
	I promised him he could glut his maw
1615	With fat chickens he would find
	On the roofbeam close behind
	The trapdoor that he must creep through.
	Isengrim laughed and hastened to
	The trapdoor, not without fright,
1620	And started groping left and right.
	But when with all his groping he found
	Nothing at all, he said, "There's ground
	For worry, Nephew, there's nothing here."

I said, "How is that, Uncle dear?
1625 Creep a little farther on.
Without pain nothing is won.
I stole the ones that sat in front."
Fooled by me he went to hunt
For poultry farther and all too far.
1630 I saw that I had got him there
Where I wanted and pushed him down.
Isengrim hurtled to the ground
And struck the floor with such a bang,
That those within the house sprang
1635 All of a sudden out of bed.
Those who lay by the fire said
That something—what they did not know—
Had fallen through the smoke-hole, so
They made a light, saw Isengrim,
1640 And straightaway struck at him
Till he was almost dead and gone.
I got him in trouble off and on,
How many times I dare not guess.
    But of all the wickedness
1645 I did to him I most repent
That I betrayed Dame Hersent,
The fair one he calls his wife
And loves better than his own life.
To her I did, God pardon me,
1650 That which I would wish to be
Undone rather than have it done.'
    Grimbert said, 'Well, go on.
If you want to confess to me
And cleanse yourself of your devilry,
1655 Your shrift should be plain and flat.
I don't know what you are driving at
With "I've betrayed his fair dame".

I cannot guess at what you aim,
Uncle, when you talk that way.'
1660   'Nephew Grimbert, would you say
It were great courtesy in me
Had I confessed thus bluntly,
"I once slept with my aunt"?
You are my nephew, you would taunt
1665   Your uncle for such churlishness!
     I've said all I should confess,
Grimbert, as far as I recall.
Give me remission now for all
My sins and set the penance, please.'
1670   Grimbert managed things with ease.
He broke a twig off a tree
And swished him, for all his devilry,
Forty times upon his fell
And then he admonished him to live well
1675   And to do good by giving alms,
Keeping vigils, singing psalms,
Fasting, observing the Lord's day,
And turning those who went astray
Back to the path of righteousness.
1680   And he should avoid excess
In everything all his days
And forswear the evil ways
Of his past, when he robbed and stole.
     Now he must cultivate his soul,
1685   Reynard, by Grimbert's advice
And go to court whatever the price.
     Now the confession is at an end
And Reynard and his nephew wend
Their way towards the king's court.
1690   Back from the road they took, a short
Distance away, there happened to be

A Black Nuns' priory,
Where geese and chickens, a mighty flock,
And many a capon and many a cock
1695 Grazed outside the fenced-in yard.
This was known to false Reynard,
That vicious creature, and he spake:
'The shortest way for us to take
Leads by yonder nunnery.'
1700 Lying thus brazenly
He led Grimbert past the place
Where in an unenclosed space
The chickens went picking left and right.
Reynard quickened at the sight.
1705 His eyes were greedily taking stock.
Apart from the others strayed a cock,
Which was both young and fat.
Reynard jumped at it, so that
The rooster's feathers flew around.
1710 Grimbert said, 'You are unsound
Of mind, Uncle! What would you do?
For the sake of a cock you would anew
Fall into all that wickedness
You've just been shriven of? I profess,
1715 You will be sorry for that ere long.'
Reynard said, 'I did wrong,
I forgot myself, dear friend.
Pray God to pardon my bad intent.
It will not happen again, of course.'
1720   Then they retraced their steps across
A narrow bridge, and more than once
Reynard threw backward a glance
Toward the spot where the chickens were.
He could not master his desire
1725 But had to go where his nature led.

If they had stricken off his head,
It would have flown towards that brood
Of chickens as far as it could.
Nephew Grimbert watched him do,
1730 And said, 'Unclean glutton you,
To let your eyes thus go astray.'
Reynard replied, 'You should not say
Things to me that upset my poise.
You make a lot of angry noise
1735 That makes my heart cringe with pain,
And disturbs the prayers I am in.
Let me read some paternosters
For the souls of the roosters,
Hens and geese that many a day
1740 I falsely caught and carried away,
Craftily stolen, I confess,
From that holy prioress.'
  Grimbert scowled, but Reynard
Kept looking back at the poultry yard,
1745 Till they regained the right road
They left for a path that Reynard showed.
That led straight to the court,
Where he expected little sport.
Reynard said, when they came near
1750 To the court, 'I shake with fear.'
  When the rumour went around
That Reynard had at last been found
And was in court in the company
Of Grimbert, the badger, you could see
1755 Even the poor and the low-born too
Getting ready to charge and sue.
Everyone on Reynard turned.
He did as if he were unconcerned,
Whatever he may have felt inside.

1760   'Nephew,' he said, 'be my guide;
        Take me along the main street.'
        Reynard stalked on proud feet
        And showed to all as bold a face
        As if he were of the royal race
1765   And innocent of wrongdoing.
        Boldly he stopped before the king
        And spoke to Noble, 'May the Lord
        Who created everything accord
        To you, O King, long happiness
1770   And great honour. I address
        Greetings to you; that is my right.
        For never did king have a knight
        So prone to serve him and so true
        As I have been and am to you.
1775   That has been proven at many a turn.
        Yet here are some in court who yearn
        To rob me of your favour, Sire,
        With lies. But you won't trust a liar.
        For which the Lord give you reward.
1780   The crown, indeed, cannot afford
        To believe too lightly everything
        That is told by rogues and knaves, O King.
        Yet, may God hear me avow,
        There are too many hypocrites now
1785   Who bring unfounded charges, and
        Gain everywhere the upper hand
        In the courts of the mighty with a lie.
        How did they ever climb so high?
        Scoundrels are by nature inclined
1790   To cause distress to the good and the kind.
        May they be punished by the Lord,
        And may he give them such reward
        As they deserve eternally.'

The king said, 'Dear me, dear me,
1795   Reynard, filthy miscreant,
How well you act the innocent.
It will avail you not a flea.
Have done with your flattery.
It will not turn me into your friend.
1800   You say you often served my end?
For that I'll give you now due reward.
And how well you kept the peace, Reynard,
Which I proclaimed and swore to enforce.'
   'Woe to me, when I think of all my loss!'
1805   Cried Chanticleer from where he stood.
The king said, 'Chanticleer, be so good
As to keep your mouth shut; leave it to me
To reply to Reynard's trickery.
Indeed, Mister thief Reynard,
1810   Of your love for me and regard
You've given ample evidence to
My envoys, at small cost to you:
Poor man Tybert and Sir Bruin,
Whose skull is still a blood-red moon.
1815   But scolding you is a waste of sound.
Your neck will pay, as will be found
Some time yet this very day.'
   Reynard answered, '*Nomine*
Patrum Christum file, if Bruin
1820   Wears on his pate a blood-red moon,
What, Sire, have I to do with that?
Because of the honey that he ate
Those louts and Lamfret cudgelled him.
However, Bruin is strong of limb.
1825   They beat and abused him? Well he should
Have taken revenge, were he any good,
Instead of fleeing in the stream.

And Tybert, the cat? What about him?
I kindly gave him bed and board.
1830 If he went out of his own accord
To rob the parish priest, and there
Got into trouble, what do I care?
If I must pay for that, my God,
I have good reason to curse my lot.
1835 Listen,' said Reynard, 'King Noble, Sire,
No doubt, whatever you desire
Be done with me, that shall be done.
Even though my cause were as clear as the sun,
You can make and break me at will,
1840 Cook me or roast me on the grill,
Or string me up or gouge my eyes,
I cannot escape you in any wise.
All beasts are in your hold.
I am puny, you are bold.
1845 I've small support, yours is great.
If you killed me, you would rate
A poor avenger in God's eyes.'
   He was still talking in this wise
When Beline, the ram, sprang up and she
1850 Who was his lady, Dame Hawee,
Who had come with him into court.
Beline said, 'Let us all report
The rest of the charges against this man.'
Bruin jumped up with all his clan,
1855 And Bruin's friend Tybert too,
And Isengrim, the bugaboo,
Forcadent, the wild boar,
Tiecelin, the raven hoar,
Pancer, the otter, and Brunel,
1860 And next the fish Putepel,
Blancart, the buck, Brishart, the bull,

Coward, the hare, the fearful,
The red squirrel, Rossel by name,
And the grey one also came,
1865   The bittern and the weasel, Madame Fine.
Chanticleer put his brood in line
And all flapped wings frantically.
The ferret, Mister Catch-a-wee,
Also joined the plaintiffs' crowd.
1870   All these went and bowed
Before their liege lord, the king,
And hauled the prisoner into the ring.
    Now there was plea and counterplea.
Beasts were never heard previously
1875   To bandy words as there did pass
Between Reynard and the beasts *en masse*.
Witness those who heard them talk.
I can't repeat them; I would balk
At having to quote word for word
1880   Everything that there was heard.
I shall therefore make it short.
Their arguments were of the finest sort.
The beasts had their charges pressed
With evidence that stood the test,
1885   As each was called on to proffer it.
The king had his high barons sit
In judgement upon the prisoner.
They were found to concur
In finding that a strong gibbet be
1890   Set up and fixed solidly
And that the criminal be strung up.
Now Reynard is out of luck.
    When Reynard's verdict had been read,
His nearest kin, with, at their head,
1895   Grimbert, the badger, went away.

None of them could bear to stay
Nor endure the ignominy
Of seeing Reynard bodily
Hanged like a common thief.
1900   Yet some of them felt little grief.
The king was a wise man.
Seeing that of Reynard's clan
So many a youth who was near kin
Of Reynard left the court in
1905   Grimbert, the badger's, company,
He meditated secretly:
    'This must not happen, on second thought.
Reynard himself is a knave, God wot,
But some of his kin are good, I know.'
1910   Then he spoke: 'Why are you so slow,
Noble Bruin and Isengrim?
There are woods and hedges here for him
To hide in should he escape his plight
Under cover of the falling night.
1915   Reynard is so crafty and fleet
That, if he but sneak away three feet,
You'll never catch him again, I fear!
He knows every turn round here.
If he must hang for his guilt,
1920   Hang him at once. Ere you have built
A gallows for him, it will be night.'
    Isengrim thought the king was right,
And said, 'There is a gallows close by,'
And, saying that, he heaved a sigh.
1925   Then Tybert, the tomcat, said to him,
'Your heart is sore, Sir Isengrim,
And I, for one, blame you not.
For it was Reynard who hatched the plot
And went himself along to where

1930 They hanged your brothers, that gallant pair,
Rumen and Ampleloin.
You can repay him in the same coin.
If you were any good, it had been done;
He would not be seeing the light of the sun.'

1935   Isengrim said to Tybert, 'See
What wisdom you are teaching me!
If we had a halter hereabout,
His neck had long ago found out
How much his buttocks might weigh.'

1940 Reynard, who long had nothing to say,
Said, 'Gentlemen, please shorten my pain.
Tybert has a rope that can stand any strain.
He got it around his neck that night
When he was in a bitter plight

1945 In the house where he bit the good
Parish priest as he stood all nude.
Sir Isengrim, get it over soon.
Were you not chosen, you and Bruin,
For the job of hanging till he be dead

1950 Your nephew Reynard, that vicious Red?
Enough thus far has been done by you,
Make Tybert go along too.
Send him up with the rope, he knows much more
Of climbing than you; spare yourself the chore.

1955 Go ahead and set the stage, you three.
To see you tarry is irksome to me.'
    Then Isengrim said to Bruin, 'I swear
By that monastic shave I wear
On the crown of my head that never before

1960 Did I hear such sound lore
As Reynard himself has given us here.
He thirsts for monastery beer.
Let us go and brew him some.'

Said Bruin, 'Cousin Tybert, come
1965   Along with us; here is the rope.
Reynard now shall pay, I hope,
For my fine cheeks and for your eye.
Let us go and hang the fellow so high
That all his friends will be put to shame.'
1970   Tybert replied, 'Yes, in the name
Of justice, let us,' and seized the rope.
'I never did so pleasant a job.'
Now the three were set to go
Whom Reynard, the fox, detested so:
1975   The wolf, and Tybert, and perforce,
Bruin, the bear, who took a course
In stealing honey that made him squirm.
Isengrim had made a firm
Resolve, that ere he left the court
1980   He would solemnly exhort
Both his male and female kin
And all who were to remain within
The court's precincts, neighbour and guest,
To keep Reynard under arrest.
1985   He made Hersent, his own wife,
Swear to him upon her life
That she would keep him under guard
And, holding on to Reynard
By his red beard, not let him free
1990   For neither prayer nor bribery,
Not for force, not for need,
Not for fear of death, indeed.
Reynard briefly made reply
That all could hear who stood near by:
1995   'Sir Isengrim, mercy fifty per cent.
You are glad my life is almost spent.
But though you declare me a miscreant,

I know well, should my aunt
Justly remember past benifice,
2000   She would never approve of this.
Sir Isengrim, uncle dear,
You take poor care of your nephew here,
And so do Tybert and Bruin, the Bear,
Since you three have stripped me bare
2005   Of honour, and have brought about
That my life will be snuffed out.
It is also due to your devilry
That, whosoever approaches me
Calls me thief and loves me not.
2010   In punishment for that, God wot,
May the three of you be cursed,
Unless you do quickly what you thirst
To have done to me. Take me away.
My heart is still as brave as aye.
2015   I can die only once, why then afraid?
My dying father would not have stayed,
For death freed him of all care.
Go then, the three of you, prepare
The gallows, and tarry not, I pray,
2020   Or else may your arse lead the way,
That legs and feet must backward go.'
    Then said Isengrim, 'Be it so.'
'So be it,' said Bruin, 'let backward tread
All who fail to go ahead.'
2025   'So be it,' said Tybert, 'Let us make haste.'
Speaking thus, the trio paced
Along the way in mighty glee,
And vied with one another playfully
In jumping over many a fence,
2030   Did Bruin and Isengrim. Tybert, since
He carried the rope, was somewhat slow

Upon his feet, and could not show
Like skill, but followed in their track.
However, he did not hang far back.
His willing heart drove him on.
       Reynard stood, when they were gone,
In silence, watching his enemies run,
Who thought to hang him would be fun.
'But it won't happen,' Reynard said,
As he stood and looked ahead
Where he saw them ply their shanks.
'My God,' he thought, 'what youthful pranks.
Let them leap, leave them alone.
If I live, they'll yet atone
For their insults and devilry,
Or there is not foxiness in me.
However, I rather see them hie
Away from my person than close by.
For they are the ones I dreaded most.
Now I will see if I can foist
A clever deceit upon the king
Which, last night, in great suffering,
I invented just before dawn.
If my cunning is not gone
But just as strong as I hope it be,
I shall yet fool his Majesty,
Although his wisdom be unsurpassed.'
       The king called for a trumpet blast
And ordered that Reynard be led away.
Reynard spoke, 'Let them first, I pray,
Prepare the gallows on which I'll swing.
And meanwhile all this gathering
Of folk shall hear me confess
In remission of my wickedness.
It is useful that all the people hear

My thefts and criminal career,
Lest they accuse later on
An innocent man of the wrong I've done.'
 The king said, 'Well, have your say.'
2070 Reynard stood like a man in dismay,
And looked at all, both far and near,
And then he spoke that all could hear:
'Here, in the king's house, there is
No one, *semmi dominis*,
2075 Friend nor foe, but has been
Sinned against by me, I ween.
Listen, folks, to your avail.
Be warned and taught by my tale
Of how I took, wretch accursed,
2080 To my wicked course at first.
I always was, from my earliest days,
A courtly cub with playful ways.
When I was weaned from the teat,
I went to play with the lambs whose bleat
2085 Attracted me. I played so long
Till at last I did one of them wrong:
I bit him and lapped the blood at once.
It tasted so good, I seized my chance,
And started to eat of the flesh, woe is me.
2090 That's how I became a gourmet, you see,
So much so that I straightaway made
For the goats where I heard them bleat in the shade.
There I killed two of the lot.
Those I ate in a secret spot.
2095 My boldness started to increase.
I killed chickens, ducks, and geese,
Wheresoever I found them loose.
When I had got my bloody tooth,
I became so fell and merciless

2100	That I killed for my mess
	Anything I found to be
	To my taste and a delicacy.
	Thereafter I came upon Isengrim.
	On a winter day I encountered him,
2105	Close to Belsele, under a tree.
	He figured he was uncle to me,
	And explained how we related were.
	We became comrades then and there.
	I remember it ruefully.
2110	There we promised each other to be
	True companions, and began
	To wander together through the land.
	He stole big, I small fare.
	Whatever we caught we would share,
2115	And sometimes we would not.
	I was ill pleased unless I got
	What I claimed as my half.
	When Isengrim caught a calf,
	Or a wither, or a tup,
2120	He'd growl and get his dander up
	And scowl at me with a face
	So sour and angry that he would chase
	Poor me away in fear and fright,
	And then he took what was mine by right.
2125	However, I did not mind a bit.
	I have so often noticed it:
	Sometimes I and my uncle lay
	In ambush and entrapped a prey,
	Ox or hog, then, if you please,
2130	He would sit down at his ease
	With seven children and his wife,
	Hersent, and have the time of his life,
	Whereas I was left to feast

On a poor rib, one of the least,
2135 After his brood had gnawed it bare,
So scant and measly was my share.
However, that caused me small distress.
Surely, if I had cared less
For my uncle who, by the way,
2140 Cares but little for me today,
I would have got enough to eat.
King, there is something which is meet
That you should know: I have and hold
So much silver and gold
2145 That seven wagon loads could not
Cart it away from the spot.'
    When the king heard him speak
Of silver and gold, he cut in quick:
'Reynard, where did you get that hoard?'
2150 'Where did I get it? I'll tell you, Lord.
If you must know what I know,
Then for neither weal nor woe
Shall it remain a mystery.
That hoard was stolen property.
2155 Had it not been stolen, though,
Murderers would long ago,
O king, have rung your death knell
To the grief of all who wish you well.'
    The queen was scared, and fearfully
2160 She cried, 'O Reynard, woe is me,
Woe me, Reynard, woe, woe!
What you are saying frightens me so.
Dear Reynard, I beg you, I pray,
By the long journey that one day
2165 Your soul must make: tell the king
The full truth, everything;
And reveal in open court

Any murder or any report
Of a murderous conspiracy
2170   Against the king, his Majesty.
Reveal to us all this evil deed.'
    Now listen how Reynard will succeed
In fooling both the king and the queen,
How he cleverly will win
2175   The king's friendship and his love,
And implicate, over and above,
Sir Bruin, and Sir Isengrim,
Who never plotted against him,
In feuds and hostility,
2180   Against his Royal Majesty.
Those lords, who were now in such arrogant mood,
Because they thought they had brewed
For Reynard an evil-tasting beer,
For them Reynard, it will appear,
2185   Is to mix in return a mead
They'll drink to their disgrace indeed.
    Putting on a dejected mien,
Reynard spoke, 'Noble Queen,
Even if you had not urged me, I—
2190   Being a man who is doomed to die—
Won't leave this burden on my soul.
If I died with it, my goal
Might be set for me in hell,
Where the tortured writhe and yell.
2195   If the king, in his mercy, will
Command the crowd to be still,
I would tell him every jot
Of that lamentable plot
Of traitorous men to murder him.
2200   The ringleaders, to my shame,
Were some of my dearest kin.

I would scarcely drag them in,
But for the fear I have of hell,
Where it is said that they shall dwell
2205 In torment who knew of a murder plot
And, in dying, told it not.'
    The king spoke, as he grew
Heavy of heart: 'Is this true?'
'True?' said Reynard, 'How can you doubt?
2210 Don't you know what I'm about?
Don't imagine, noble King,
Although I'm but a starveling,
That I could wink at such a crime.
Do you think this is a time
2215 For me to take a lie along
On my long journey? That were wrong.'
    At the queen's request, who was afraid
For the king's safety, he forbade
By proclamation that any in court
2220 Should be so bold as to say aught
Were it only the slightest word,
Until everyone had heard
All that Reynard would reveal.
All fell silent at that appeal.
2225 The king said, 'Reynard, take the floor.'
Reynard knew tricks galore.
He felt sure, he would pull through.
He spoke: 'Be silent, all of you.
Since this is the king's behest,
2230 I shall, without any brief, attest
In open court to the treachery,
Sparing none, whosoever he be,
I am in duty bound to name.
If the cap fits, the more is the shame.'
2235   Now you shall hear how that liar,

Reynard, accuses his earthly sire,
Of treason and, among the rest,
One of his kin whom he liked best.
That was Grimbert, the badger, one
2240   Whom Reynard could always count upon.
Reynard had his reason for this:
They would sooner believe the treacheries
He planned to lay to his foes
If he also accused those
2245   Of his own kin of complicity.
Now listen how he began his plea:
He said, 'One day, years agone,
My father happened to come upon
King Ermerik's hoard, which he found
2250   Hidden somewhere underground.
After that discovery
My father turned suddenly
So overbearing and so proud
That he despised and disavowed
2255   His former companions from that day.
He sent Tybert the cat away
Into the wild Ardennes, where
He paid a visit to Bruin, the bear;
He said to him, "God be with you", and
2260   Told him to come to Flanders land
If he wanted to be king.
That was for Bruin a good tiding.
He had longed to be king many a day.
To Flanders he went straightaway
2265   And came into the sweet land of Waes,
Where he knew my father was.
My father called wise Grimbert in
And also the hoary Isengrim.
That made five with Tybert the cat.

2270 They passed through a village—the name of that
Was Hyft—and between Hyft and Ghent
The five of them held a parliament
In a moon-and-starless night.
And there they swore, by the devil's might
2275 And by the power of my father's hoard,
All five of them death to the lord
Their king, upon that wild moor.
But this will amaze you, I am sure:
On Isengrim's head the five of them there
2280 Swore an oath that Bruin the bear
Would be made king and take the crown
Upon the throne within the town
Of Aix-la-Chapelle. And if one
Or other of King Noble's clan
2285 Should oppose it, my father told
His accomplices that with his gold
He'd make them suffer a reverse
So that they would have the worse.
How do I know? Listen to me:
2290 My cousin, the badger, happened to be,
One early morning, slightly lit,
Having tasted wine and too much of it,
And he described the plot they'd made,
In confidence, from a to z,
2295 To my wife, Dame Hermelin
As the two went sauntering
Across the heath. My wife is clever,
And promised Grimbert she would never
Tell the story to any one.
2300 But as soon as she had run
Into the forest and found me
She gave it away instantly,
Albeit in strict confidence.

She mentioned by way of evidence,
2305   Details that I knew were right,
So that my hair, for very fright,
Stood on end all over my skin,
And I felt my heart within
Turn suddenly icy cold.
2310   I recalled how of old
The frogs were living in liberty,
And how they grumbled they were too free
And much in need of restraint.
They got together and made complaint
2315   With much croaking, and asked God
To let them have, under his rod,
A king who would keep them controlled.
That was the prayer of young and old,
With loud croaking, throughout the bogs.
2320   God granted unto the frogs
Their wish, upon a day in spring,
And sent the stork to be their king,
By whom they were bitten and devoured
Everywhere as he scoured
2325   The fields and the ponds. No matter where
He happened to catch them, he wouldn't spare
A single one, whether small or great.
Then they moaned, but it was too late.
It was too late, I'll tell you why.
2330   They who were free in days gone by
Shall remain irrevocably
Mere chattel and property
And live in everlasting awe
Of King Stork's cruel law.
2335   Listen, ye men, great and small,
I was afraid that for us all
A similar fate might be in store.

Thus I worried, thus I bore
A burden of care for your good,
2340   For which you show small gratitude.
        Bruin, I knew, was bad as could be,
And full of great depravity.
Were he to lord it over us,
That would, I thought, be calamitous.
2345   Then all of us would be forlorn.
I knew the king to be well born,
Kind and good in thought and deed,
And merciful to all our breed.
It seemed, from every point of view,
2350   A bad exchange, which, I knew,
Would not, however you looked at it,
Redound to our honour or benefit.
This matter would not let me rest.
My heart was troubled and depressed,
2355   Pondering how so wicked a plot
Could be foiled, lest a sot,
A boorish glutton, be acclaimed
King, as he whom I'm ashamed
To call father, planned to do.
2360   I prayed God ever anew
That he preserve my lord and stay
His world honour and royal sway.
        I was aware, to be sure,
That, if my father could secure
2365   His treasure trove, he would with ease,
Aided by his accomplices,
Overthrow your Majesty.
I pondered unceasingly,
And often wondered how I might
2370   Discover the secret site
Where my father's treasure lay.

I kept close watch night and day,
And lay in wait for my sire
In many a bush, in many a briar,
2375　　Both in field and in wood,
Wherever my sly old man pursued
His prey or chose to run or creep,
Were it dry, or were it deep,
Were it by day, were it by night.
2380　　I always kept him within sight.
　　　　One day luck did me a good turn:
I lay concealed under green fern,
Sprawling flat upon the ground
And sore because I had not found
2385　　The treasure I was longing for.
And there, suddenly, I saw
My father sneaking out of a hole.
Then I had hope of reaching my goal,
Seeing the ruse he resorted to.
2390　　I'll tell you what I saw him do.
I noticed that, as soon as he stole
Cautiously out of the hole
He looked around to satisfy
Himself that nobody was near by.
2395　　And when he did not see a soul,
He gathered sand to stop the hole
And made it even with the rest,
Calling the day his very best.
He did not know I was watching it.
2400　　I also saw that, ere he quit,
He swept the ground with his tail
Where his feet had left a trail,
And covered his spoor with the sand.
The old one always was a good hand
2405　　At ruses and I learnt some there

Of which I'd never been aware.
Thus my father, the sly old fox,
Left for the village, where the cocks
And the fat chickens ran about.

2410   As soon as I dared come out,
I leapt up and ran to the hole.
I had not lost sight of my goal.
I got to it quickly, and began
Immediately to scrape the sand

2415   With my forepaws and crept in.
There I found immense gain!
There I found silver and gold!
Even those who are old
Never saw so much wealth in a heap.

2420   Then there was for me no sleep.
I carried and dragged night and day,
Without a cart, without a dray,
Both at daytime and by night,
Aided only by my own might

2525   And by my wife, Dame Hermeline.
The two of us endured great pain
Before we had brought the famous hoard
Somewhere else where it was stored
More conveniently for us.

2430   We took it, without any fuss,
To a hole under a ditch.
Never had I been so rich!
    And what do you think those did, meantime,
Who had plotted that treacherous crime?

2435   I will tell you: Bruin, the bear,
Sent greetings, by trusted messenger,
Throughout the land and offered much
Ready money to all such
As were willing to serve for pay.

2440 He promised them he would give away
Silver and gold with lavish hand.
It was my father who tramped the land
To deliver Sir Bruin's brief.
He didn't suspect that a thief
2445 Had discovered his treasury
And plundered it so thoroughly
That not three pennies of it were found
Wherewith to pay for London town,
If to buy London was his intent.
2450 His tramping gained him not a cent.
　　When my father, tramping around
'Tween Elbe and Somme, had covered the ground
In all directions and had won
Many a sturdy yeoman
2455 With the bait of his gold,
Who would come to his aid, when told,
At the first summer breeze,
He joined again his accomplices,
Sir Bruin and the other three.
2460 He told them of the jeopardy
He was in, and the many close calls
He had at the foot of towering walls
Of castles in distant Saxony,
Where the hunters merrily
2465 Rode daily after him with the pack,
So that he barely saved his back.
He told them these stories for the fun.
Then my father read to Bruin
Letters which delighted him,
2470 For twelve hundred of Isengrim
His kin were listed there by name,
All of sharp-clawed, wide-mouthed fame,
But not the cats and the bears, for they

Were to be all in Bruin's pay,
2475 Nor the fox and badger yeomanry
From Thuringia and Saxony.
These had all sworn to spring
To the support of Bruin for king,
On condition they got at once
2480 Three weeks' pay in advance.
They would with might and main appear
At the first summons from Bruin the bear.
But nothing came of it, thanks to me.
When my father, finally,
2485 Had made his report, he hastened away
To inspect the hole where his treasure lay.
And when he arrived, expecting to find
All the treasure he left behind,
He found that burglars had forced the place
2490 And of his treasure not a trace.
No need to say more of this. My sire,
At sight of it, shook with ire
And hanged himself for misery.
Thus, thanks to my strategy,
2495 Bruin's plot came to naught.
See now to what pass I'm brought:
Glutton Bruin and Isengrim
Have the King's ear and counsel him,
As is clear to everyone,
2500 And poor man Reynard is undone.'
    Noble, the king, who was just as keen
To get hold of the treasure as was the queen,
Led Reynard away outside the court,
And both begged him to be a good sport
2505 And show them where his hoard was hid.
Reynard listened to them and said,
'Should I show my treasury

To those who want to gibbet me?
I'd be mad if I did.'
2510 'No, Reynard,' the queen said,
'My lord, the king, will set you free
And will temper with amity
For once and all his angry mood;
And you shall be wise and good
2515 Hereafter and loyal to my lord.'
Reynard said, 'It's an accord,
Madame, if His Majesty
Now, in your presence, promise me
To give me his patronage
2520 And to cancel the black page
Of my misdeeds; in return for that
I will show the king the spot
Where I have my treasury.'
The king answered, 'I would be
2525 Deranged if I believed Reynard.
He is a robber and blackguard.
His falsehood is bred in the bone.'
The queen spoke in a different tone:
'No, lord, you can trust him, I can tell.
2530 He was, indeed, fierce and fell.
But he isn't now what he used to be.
He charged the badger—didn't he?—
And his own father—what is more—
With murder, though there are a score
2535 Of beasts he might have accused instead,
If he were still ill-bred
Or vicious or treacherous and mean.'
Then said the king, 'Noble queen,
If you dare counsel me,
2540 Though it turn out fatally,
I will by your encouragement

Make this pact and covenant
Upon the faith that Reynard swore.
But I tell him, if ever more
2545 He commits wickedness,
His kin shall have to make redress,
Down to the tenth degree.'
　　Reynard's heart was full of glee
When he saw he had fooled them both.
2550 He said, 'If I didn't swear that oath,
I'd be a fool as ever you saw.'
　　Then the king took a straw
And forgave Reynard the crime
His father committed in his time
2555 And also his own knavery.
It is no cause of wonder to me
That Reynard, in that hour, was glad,
Seeing the narrow escape he had.
　　When Reynard found himself reprieved,
2560 He was exceedingly relieved
And said, 'King, noble lord,
God requite the boon you accord
To me and to my courtly wife,
Who has been loyal all her life.
2565 You do me honour, I realize,
And so much good in many a guise
That there is no one under the sun
To whom I would rather give the run
Of my treasure trove than to thee,
2570 O queen, and to thy Majesty.'
Reynard took a straw and said,
'By this token I now have laid
Into thy hand that rich hoard
That once Ermerik owned, my Lord.'
2575 The king accepted the straw from him

And thanked him so much that it would seem
He thought, 'He gives me omnipotence.'
　　Reynard's joy was so intense,
One almost saw it in his face,
2580　When the king with so much grace
Did his will obediently.
Reynard said, 'Lord, please to be
Attentive to what I have to say.
In East Flanders, far away,
2585　Stands a forest called Hulsterloe.
You'll have a windfall, King, I know,
If you can remember it:
A winding brook called Criekenpit
Runs south-west of it near by.
2590　You need not fear I'm telling a lie,
I won't conceal the truth, Lord King,
There is not any living thing
In that desolate wilderness.
Sometimes half a year will pass—
2595　It's gospel truth that I speak—
That not a soul comes to the creek,
Neither a man nor his wife,
Not a creature that has life,
Except the owl and the thrush
2600　That nestle there among the brush
Or little birds of different kind
That lost their way and cannot find
The places where they want to be.
There lies my treasure, your majesty.
2605　The place is called Criekenpit.
It will pay to remember it.
Go to that spot, you and the queen.
You can't trust anyone, I mean
To go on that errand, even though

2610 You ask or order them to go.
      You ought yourselves to go and seek
      The treasure; and when you reach the creek
      You'll find there seven young birch trees.
      Now mark this well, Your Majesties,
2615 The tree that stands nearest the brook,
      That's the one for which you must look.
      For under it the treasure is hid.
      There you must dig and scrape amid
      Some moss at one side of the tree.
2620 There you will find much jewellery
      Of gold, many a precious thing.
      The crown that Ermerik, the king,
      Used to wear is one of these,
      And many preciosities,
2625 Stones and costly things of gold.
      King, you would not let them be sold
      For a thousand pounds. When that rich pile
      Is yours, you'll think many a while,
      "O my Reynard, faithful fox,
2630 Who buried there under the moss
      This treasure trove so artfully,
      May God bless you wherever you be."'
          Then the king was heard to say,
      'If I must travel all that way,
2635 You must bear me company,
      Reynard, and must render me
      Assistance in digging up your hoard.
      I could not, of my own accord,
      Find the way to that spot.
2640 You mentioned Aken, did you not?
      And Paris. Is it near those two?
      And if it is right what I think of you,
      You are bragging, Reynard, and flattering me.

This Criekenpit is sure to be,
2645   I warrant, a fictitious name.'
           Reynard feared he might spoil his game
       And answered Noble angrily,
       'Yes, yes, Your Majesty,
       Just as near as Cologne to May.
2650   Do you expect me, King, to say
       That the Ly is where the Jordan flows?
       I'll proffer proof that clearly shows
       The truth of this as will appear.'
       He called aloud, 'Coward, come here,
2655   Come and stand before the king.'
       All the beasts were wondering
       What was to happen and were intent.
       In fear and trembling Coward went
       Wondering what the king might want.
2660   Said Reynard, 'Why do you tremble? Don't.
       Have no fear, or are you cold?
       The king must have the truth told.
       Tell it by the faith that is due
       To Gente, our gracious queen, and to
2665   Noble, the King, His Majesty.'
       Coward said, 'God's curses be
       Upon my head if I should lie,
       Although I had to testify
       Of murder and knew in advance
2670   It would cost me my life to give evidence.
       For you challenge me by the faith I swore
       To my dear lady heretofore
       And to my lord, Noble, the king.'
       Reynard said, 'This is the thing
2675   He wants to know: Where is Criekenpit?'
       'Sire, I would be most dull of wit,'
       Said Coward, 'if I did not know.

Is it not close to Hulsterloe,
On the moor, in the wilderness?
2680 I have suffered much distress,
Much hunger, and much cold,
And privations manifold
So many a day at Criekenpit
That I shall always remember it.
2685 Do you think I could forget
That the beagle Simonet
Made his counterfeit money there,
With which he paid for his daily fare,
He and his cronies? That must have been
2690 Ere Rine and I agreed, I ween,
To keep each other company.
He often paid my schoolbook fee.'
      'Alas, sweet Rine,' Reynard said,
'Dear companion, nobly-bred
2695 Harrier, I wish you could appear
Before these beasts and let them hear
In verse, could it be told in rhyme,
That I never at any time
Had the temerity to do
2700 Anything one might construe
As a crime deserving the king's ire.
Coward,' said Reynard, 'you may retire
Among yonder fellows; quick, be gone.
There is nothing further whereupon
2705 My lord the king would question you.'
      Coward turned and withdrew
From the king's council room.
Said Reynard, 'Sire, may I presume
To ask you, did I speak truthfully?'
2710 'Yes, I wronged you, forgive it me,
Reynard, with my distrust.

Reynard, dear friend, now you must
Make arrangements for going with me
To the brook where stands the birch tree
2715 Under which you buried the hoard.'
'That would be wonderful, my Lord.
You know I would only be too glad,
Sire,' said Reynard, 'if I had
Permission to go in your company,
2720 Such as we both like to be
And as you are, Lord: without sin.
But no, I confess for my discipline,
Although I say it to my shame:
When Isengrim, in the devil's name,
2725 Entered the order heretofore
And was shaved a monk, it made him sore
To feed his hunger on a monkish diet.
What six monks ate could not satisfy it.
He complained he was starving, poor Isengrim,
2730 And groaned till I took pity on him.
When he fell ill and pined away,
I, being his kinsman, was in dismay,
And told him to flee. The Vatican
Struck me for that with the papal ban.
2735 Tomorrow at sunrise I will leave
For Rome to ask for a reprieve.
From Rome I'll go to the Holy Land,
And not until I am un-banned
And fit to keep you company
2740 Without scathe to your honour and dignity
Shall I return from Palestine,
If ever I come home again.
It would be an unseemly thing
For me to appear, my Lord and King,
2745 In the company of your Majesty

As long as—may God chasten me—
I shall remain in the church's ban.'
    The king said, 'Tell me, Reynard, when
Did the ban strike you?' Reynard said,
2750   "Three years ago the synod laid
In plenary session the church's ban
On my guilty head before Hereman,
The Deacon.' The king said, 'Since you are
Under the ban, I must keep far
2755   Away from you to avoid disgrace.
I shall take Coward in your place,
Or some one else, to Criekenpit.
And don't be slow—I insist on it—
In leaving for the Vatican,
2760   Where they will clear you of the ban.'
    Reynard said, 'I won't, my Lord.
Tomorrow I shall go Rome-ward,
If nothing adverse happen to me.'
    The king said, 'Reynard, you seem to be
2765   Well-intentioned. God permit
That you shall accomplish it
In such a way as will accrue
To the profit of all, of me and you.'
    When this talk was at an end,
2770   Noble, the king, took his stand
On a high stage piled up of stone
On which he used to stand alone
When he presided at court of law.
All around in the grass he saw
2775   The beasts sit ring-wise, every one
In the place his birth laid claim upon.
Reynard stood beside the queen.
Now hear how Noble will begin
To address the court in a regal tone:

2780	'Hear, all of you, not the great alone
	And the rich, but also the poor and the small,
	My barons and my fellows all.
	Reynard has come here into court
	Intending—for which I praise the Lord—
2785	To turn over a new leaf.
	The queen holds for him a brief
	And has pleaded so well that I
	Have become his ally.
	My rancour towards him is all gone.
2790	I've given him absolution
	Of life and death penalties.
	I command that Reynard be left in peace.
	Reynard be left in peace, I ordain,
	He be left in peace, I say again.
2795	And I command all of you,
	On pain of death, that you do
	Honour to Reynard and to his wife
	And children, wherever you meet in life,
	Be it by night, be it by day.
2800	Henceforth I will not pay
	Attention to charges any more.
	Although he was ruthless heretofore,
	He'll mend his ways, I'll tell you how.
	Early tomorrow, that is his vow,
2805	He'll leave with bag and staff his home
	And go on a pilgrimage to Rome
	And the Holy Land, and he'll remain
	In Palestine, nor come back again,
	Until he has received as meed
2810	Remission of every sinful deed.'
	The raven Tiecelin, hearing that,
	Flew to the spot where he always sat,
	The gallows, where he found the three

Companions, and said—now listen to me—
2815 'Caitiffs, what are you doing here?
Reynard is chief butler and dear
To the king at court and powerful.
The king has acquitted him in full
Of all the charges he had to face,
2820 And the three of you are in disgrace.'
Isengrim was curt of mien
When he replied to Tiecelin:
'I bet, Sir Raven, that's a lie,'
And scampered off, followed by
2825 Sir Bruin, the bear, on sore paws.
Both ran without a pause
In their haste to reach the king.
Tybert sat like a frightened thing
Stockstill on the gallows tree.
2830 He was in such an agony
Of fear for his shaggy chest
That he gladly would have left
Unavenged the eye he lost
In the priest's barn, to his cost,
2835 If Reynard and he were friends anew.
In his fear he knew not what to do
But sit upon the gallows tree.
He lamented to God repeatedly
That he ever knew Reynard.
2840 Isengrim, without any regard
For the queen, pushed to where she stood
And spoke to her in an ugly mood
Against Reynard, taking such liberty
That Noble, the king, angrily
2845 Ordered Isengrim and Bruin
To be arrested. Both were soon
Seized and bound forcibly.

You never saw greater infamy
Done to mad dogs than was done to him,
2850 Sir Bruin, and to Sir Isengrim.
They were treated as loathsome rogues.
Both were bound with such strong ropes
That all during that day and night,
However hard they tried,
2855 They could not move a single limb.
Now hear what he will do to them.
    Reynard, whose hatred of them was fell,
Obtained that a strip of fell
Was cut off Bruin's back,
2860 Which they gave him for a sack,
A square foot in size. Thus clad
Reynard could travel, if he had
Two pairs of solid shoes.
Now listen what he does
2865 To get hold of a double pair.
He whispered into the queen's ear,
'Lady, I am your pilgrim.
Here is my uncle, Sir Isengrim.
He possesses four solid shoes.
2870 Allow me to borrow two of those
And I will take your soul in trust.
You know, lady, a pilgrim must
Remember in his prayers the good
He got from others in gratitude.
2875 You must shoe your soul on me.
Call Hersent, my aunt, and see
That she give me two of her shoes.
It's perfectly proper that she does:
She sits at home and takes her ease.'
2880   Gente, the queen, replied to this:
'Reynard, you cannot do without.

You must have shoes, for you're about
To travel abroad in God's keep,
Through forests and over mountains steep
2885 And set your feet on stubble and stone.
And the wolf his shoes alone
Would be fitting for your need.
They are so thick and solid, indeed,
The shoes Hersent and Isengrim wear.
2890 Each must give you one pair
For the journey you must make,
Although their lives should be at stake.'
 Thus that false pilgrim
Obtained that Isengrim
2895 Lost of both his forepaws
All the skin, from his claws
Up to the bend with which he kneeled.
You never saw a falcon seeled
Who kept stiller every limb
2900 Than he did, Sir Isengrim,
When he was cruelly unshod
So that his legs were bathed in blood.
 When Isengrim had lost his shoes,
Dame Hersent had to lose
2905 Hers as well, and had to go
And lie on the grass, full of woe,
And let them strip off her fell,
And not only that, but the claws as well,
The claws of both her hind feet.
2910 Reynard thought, that was sweet.
The sight cheered his sad soul.
But listen how he played his role
Of nephew: 'Aunt, dear aunt,' he said,
'How oft you've been discomforted
2915 For my sake, I must admit.

I am sorry to be the cause of it.
But this I like, I tell you why:
You are—I'm telling you no lie—
The dearest to me of all my kin.
2920   That's why I plan to travel in
Your shoes. You'll share that way, God wot,
In the indulgence to be got
And in the pardon they will grant
To me in the Holy Land, dear aunt,
2925   When I arrive there in your shoes.'
    Dame Hersent could barely use
Her voice, she suffered such agony.
'Reynard,' she said, 'God's vengeance be
Upon you for forcing on us your will.'
2930   Isengrim remained all still.
Neither did Bruin utter a sound,
Though both were dejected and cast down.
They lay there bound and badly hurt.
And I dare say, if Tybert
2935   Had been there too, the tomcat,
Reynard, I am sure of that,
Would've seen to it that he should stay
As little out of harm's way.
Why spin it out? There's nothing to say
2940   Except that at the break of day
Reynard had his shoes oiled
In which, before, Isengrim toiled
And his wife, Dame Hersent,
And had them very firmly pinned
2945   On to his feet. Then he went
To visit the king, and Lady Gente,
Who was his queen; and unctuously
He spoke to them as you shall see:
    'Lord, God give you good day

2950 And to my lady, on whom I may,
With full right, bestow my praise.
Let Reynard, your servant, be given, please,
His bag and staff, and let him go.'
    The king summoned, nothing slow,
2955 His court chaplain, Beline, the ram.
He came and said, 'Sire, here I am.'
Said the king, 'You see this pilgrim.
Read him a mass, and hand him
His bag and staff. Do as I say,'
2960 'Lord, King, I dare not obey.'
Answered Beline to His Majesty.
'Reynard himself, recently,
Admitted he was in the papal ban.'
The king replied, 'What of it, good man?
2965 It is Master Giles I rely upon.
He says, if one man alone had done
Sins as many as all living men's,
He would be able yet to cleanse
Himself if he abandon wrong
2970 And make confession and go along,
By way of penance, across the sea
To the Holy Land.' 'Your Majesty,'
Beline replied unto the king,
'I'll do for Reynard not a thing
2975 In spiritual ministration, or
You must swear to declare me quit before
Bishop and deacon of all blame.'
'I won't make you in seven weeks the same
Request,' the king said in reply.
2980 'I would rather you hung by the neck than that I
Had asked a favour of you today.'
Beline, on hearing King Noble say
These words and seeing him thus irate,

Took fright, and in an anxious state,
2985 Which made him shake with fear and falter,
Went away to prepare his altar
And began to sing and pray
All that he thought would suit the day.
    When the chaplain, the ram Beline,
2990 Had performed with pious mien
The day's office, he hung a sack
Fashioned out of Bruin's back
Around the neck of Reynard.
He also handed the blackguard
2995 A staff to support him on the way.
Thus equipped with this array
He was all set for journeying.
Then he looked towards the king.
Crocodile tears trickled down
3000 Along his whiskers on the ground,
As if he were wretched in his heart.
If regret made him smart,
It was because he had not designed
For all of those whom he left behind
3005 Like punishment as Isengrim
And Bruin had received from him,
If he had only had better success.
He stood and begged them nevertheless
That they would pray as faithfully
3010 For him as they would wish that he
Would pray for them in return.
This leave-taking made Reynard squirm,
For he was anxious to be gone.
He was always set upon
3015 By fear, as one who knows his debt.
    The king spoke, 'I regret,
Reynard, that you are so pressed.'

'It's time, my Lord. For it is best
Not to delay the good one plans.
3020   Give me leave, Sire, to go hence.'
The king said, 'God be your support.'
And commanded all the court
To offer conduct to the fox,
Except the prisoners in the stocks.
3025   Now Reynard is a pilgrim,
And his uncle, Sir Isengrim,
Is bound and sore with wounds and care,
Together with Sir Bruin, the bear.
I have a notion and would guess
3030   That there is none so humourless
Between Polanen and the isle
Of Schouwen as not to laugh or smile,
Though he had reason for discontent,
Had he seen Reynard as he went
3035   Accoutred thus curiously:
The sack he slung comfortably
Around his neck, the staff he bore,
The shoes, one, two, three, four,
Which he had tied unto his feet,
3040   Made up together a complete
Pilgrim's outfit; he looked the part.
Reynard laughed down in his heart
Because they all came along,
Crowding round him in a throng,
3045   Who first had held him in despite.
He said, 'Sire, it is not right
That you go with me all this way.
You invite, I fear, some foul play.
Two murderous knaves are in your power.
3050   Suppose, they escaped this very hour?
You'd have to be on your guard much more

Than you ever were before.
Sire, let me go, goodbye.'
   Having said this, he rose high
3055 On his hindlegs begging all
The assembled beasts, the big and the small,
To offer up a daily prayer
For him, if they would have due share
In the reward for his good deeds.
3060 They said they would, in telling their beads,
Remember him, as they were bid.
   Listen now what Reynard did
As he parted from the king.
He showed a grief so harrowing
3065 That some took pity on poor Reynard.
Mournfully he farewelled Coward:
'Must we be parted, woe is me!
Please God, you bear me company,
And friend Beline, the ram, too.
3070 I never was angry with him or you.
Walk on a little farther with me.
You're well-behaved and known to be
Kindly disposed and without blame,
And sued by none. No trace of shame
3075 Attaches to either him or you.
You live the way I used to do
When my home was a hermit's cell.
When you've leaves and grass, all's well.
For you have no desire to eat
3080 Either chunks of bread or meat,
Or any other special fare.'
   With such flattery the pair
Were fooled by him and prevailed upon
To stay with Reynard and saunter on
3085 Till they arrived at his estate

Of Maupertuis in front of the gate.
Reynard, in front of the gate, addressed
Beline, the ram: 'Dear cousin, rest,
And stay in the open here alone.
3090   I must go in and visit my own.
Coward shall go in with me.
Beseech him, Sir Beline, that he
Dry Dame Hermeline's tears
And those of her whelps, the little dears,
3095   When I take leave of my family.'
    Beline said, 'I beg him fervently
That he console them in their despair.'
Reynard addressed to Coward, the hare,
Cajolery and flattery
3100   In such a rich variety
That Coward was tempted by his cant
To enter his subterranean haunt.
When they came inside his lair,
Reynard, the fox, and Coward, the hare,
3105   They found Dame Hermeline among
A litter of her little young.
She was worried and on her guard,
For she imagined that Reynard
Had been hanged. Seeing him
3110   Coming home as a pilgrim
Equipped with shoes and sack and staff,
She wondered and began to laugh.
She was glad and said presently,
'Reynard dear, how did you get free?'
3115   'I was arrested in court, but lo!
Noble, the king, let me go.
I must become a pilgrim.
Sir Bruin and Sir Isengrim
Have become hostages for me.

3120	The king has given us, glory be!
	Coward as compensation, to do
	With him as pleases me and you.
	The king himself admitted the fact
	That it was Coward who attacked
3125	Us first in court with a false charge.
	By the faith I must discharge,
	My wife, Dame Hermeline, to you,
	Coward's penalty is now due.
	I have just cause for chastisement.'
3130	When Coward perceived his intent,
	He turned round and would have fled.
	Too late! for Reynard got ahead
	Of Coward and cut off the gate.
	He seized him by the throat to sate
3135	His murderous lust; and piteously
	Coward cried, 'Help me,
	Beline, where are you? leave me not!
	Reynard bites me in the throat!'
	But his crying was soon done,
3140	For the hare was set upon
	By Reynard, who killed him with one bite.
	'Now we'll sate our appetite,'
	Reynard said, 'with this good, fat hare.'
	His little whelps ran to the fare
3145	Helterskelter, and started to feed.
	Their mourning was but slight, indeed,
	For the loss of Coward's life.
	Hermeline, Reynard's wife,
	Ate of the meat and drank no less
3150	Of the blood. How often did she bless
	Noble, the king, who had been so good
	As to regale her little brood
	So lavishly with a fine meal.

Said Reynard, 'He likes to give us our fill.
3155   If only God will let him live,
King Noble would be glad to give
A present to us for which, I'm told,
He would not pay seven marks of gold.'
'What present is that?' asked Hermeline.
3160   Reynard said, 'It is a line,
Two uprights and a crossbeam.
But if I can I shall cross him
And flee before two days are past
To a place where I shall mind the blast
3165   Of his wrath as little as he will mine.'
'And where is that?' asked Hermeline.
    Reynard said, 'I'll tell you where.
I know a desert rugged and bare
Of all but thistle, heather and ling.
3170   And there is plenty of everything
That we shall need for a lair and food:
Pheasants, partridges ... I could
Not mention all the birds by name.
Dame Hermeline, suppose you came
3175   Away with me and followed me there.
We might stay there seven year
And wander around in obscurity
And live in the lap of luxury
Ere they discovered whither we flew.
3180   Though I said more, it would all be true.'
    'O Reynard, Reynard,' answered she,
'You talk of travail, it seems to me,
That would be wasted. For didn't you say
That you had sworn not to stay
3185   In this country from now on
Until as a pilgrim you had gone
To the Holy Land with staff and sack?'

Reynard gave this answer back:
'The more one has sworn, the more must be torn.
3190 Once I was told by a man well-born
Whom I consulted for advice,
A forced oath is valueless.
My going to that holy place
As pilgrim would not mend my case,
3195 Not by the worth of an egg yolk.
I promised the king,' Reynard spoke,
'A treasure that I cannot produce.
I have been playing fast and loose,
And when he discovers presently
3200 That he was deceived by me,
He will hate me much more
Than he ever did before.
So I think it's just as well
For me to abscond as to sail
3205 To the Holy Land,' Reynard declared.
'And God curse my reddish beard
(Whatsoever happen to me)
If I ever persuaded be
By the badger or the cat
3210 Or Bruin who summoned me to that,
Neither for profit nor for pain,
To throw myself once again
On the king's mercy in time to be.
I've suffered too much agony.'

3215   Beline, the ram, became dismayed
Because his comrade Coward stayed
So long within and left him alone.
He bellowed in an angry tone:
'Coward, what the devil is up?
3220 How long will Reynard pass the cup?
Why don't you come out? Let us go!'

149

Reynard, hearing him rage so,
Went outside to Beline
And spoke to him with gentle mien:
3225 'My dear Sir, you must not mind
Nor rage that Coward felt inclined
For a chat with me and his aunt.
This is quite normal—yet if you can't
Wait any longer, Coward said
3230 You had better go ahead
At a slow, leisurely pace.
Coward must tarry in this place
A little while with his kin,
His poor aunt, Dame Hermeline,
3235 And her whelps, who are making moan
Because they know I'll soon be gone.'
Beline said, 'Now confess,
Sir Reynard, what wickedness
Have you done to Coward, the hare?
3240 I thought I heard him in your lair
Cry aloud to me for aid.'
'What are you talking of?' Reynard said.
'Don't be a fool, God forbid.
I well tell you what we did.
3245 When we two had gone in
And I told Hermeline
That I was going oversea,
She was in great misery
And fell into a fainting fit.
3250 Coward, who witnessed it,
Cried, "Beline, generous thane,
Come and help me ease the pain
Of my aunt; she has fainted away!"
He never cried louder, I dare say.'
3255 Then said Beline, 'And was that all?

I heard, indeed, Coward call
So fearfully, I was afraid
That he was hurt, maybe, or dead.'
Reynard said, 'No, Beline,
3260   I would rather, had there been
A mishap, that my wife and brood
Suffered than that Coward should.'
     Reynard said, 'Did you, by the way,
Hear the king yesterday,
3265   In front of many of his men,
Command me that I should pen
A letter to him before I start?
Will you deliver it on my part?
It is all written and ready to go.'
3270   Beline replied, 'I don't know.
Could I be sure that it will be
A loyal message, you'll easily
Persuade me to take it to the king,
Provided that I had something
3275   In which to carry it about.'
Said Reynard, 'You shall not be without.
Rather than keep the king's letter back,
I would present you with this sack
Which I carry, Sir Beline,
3280   And, after I've put the letter in,
Hang it around your neck, dear friend.
This letter, I swear, will serve your end,
And earn you honour and gratitude
From the king, my lord, to whom you should
3285   Be very welcome, I dare say.'
     Beline did not say him nay.
Reynard went into his cave
And, when he emerged again, he gave
To his friend, Sir Beline,

3290 Coward's head stuck within
The pilgrim's sack; and—being versed
In wicked wiles he always nursed—
He hung it around Beline's neck,
Warning him that he should check
3295 His curiosity to know
The contents if he wanted to show
His faith to the king and win his grace.
The letter was in a secret place,
Inside the sack, Reynard said.
3300 Did he want to be thought talented,
And did he love his lord, the king?
Then he should say that the lettering
Of this missive was his alone,
And his the tenor and the tone.
3305 The king would show him his gratitude.
   Beline leapt from where he stood
Nearly as high as half a yard
On hearing this promise from Reynard,
So glad he was about this thing,
3310 Which would turn out to his undoing.
   'Sir Reynard,' said Beline,
'Now, indeed, it is clearly seen,
You do me honour. Through your support
I'll win great praise from all at court
3315 When they know I can compose
In choice words and fluent prose,
Although I can't, if the truth be told.
Many a man has been extolled,
It's often said, if God but will,
3320 For things in which he had slight skill.'
   Then Beline said, 'Reynard,
What do you think, should Coward
Journey back with me to court?'

'No, Beline,' was Reynard's retort,
3325 'He'll follow by the trail you take.
He is not ready yet to make
The journey. Go ahead at an easy pace.
Coward must hear about a case
That is not yet known to any one.'
3330 'Goodbye, Reynard, I must be gone,'
Said Beline, and went his way.
    Now hear how Reynard employed his day.
He went back into his place
And said, 'We shall have to face
3335 A riot and misery if we stay here.
Get yourself ready, Hermeline dear,
And my children, all the lot.
Follow, your father will fail you not.
Let us try to get away.'
3340   There was not a moment's delay,
But all the family took the road
Which Hermeline and Reynard showed
To their whelps. The whole band
Started out for the waste land.
3345   Sir Beline, the ram, made haste
So very fast that he faced
The court in the early afternoon.
The king noticed very soon
That Beline brought back the sack
3350 That had been cut from Bruin's back
With so much torture to the bear.
He spoke at once to Beline: 'Where,
Sir Beline, have you been so long?
Where is Reynard? This sack does not belong
3355 To you. Why doesn't he carry that thing?'
Beline answered, 'My lord and king,
I can tell you as far as I know.

When Reynard was all set to go
And ready to leave his stronghold,
3360 He said to me he had been told
To write a letter to you, O King,
And requested that I should bring
The letter to court for love of you.
I said I would carry more than a few
3365 For love of Your Majesty to court.
Since Reynard had not any sort
Of thing to carry the letter in
He brought me this sack and said, "Herein
Is the letter stuck away."
3370 He never heard, king, I dare say,
Of a better poet than me.
I wrote this letter for him, you see,
Be it to my credit or to my shame.
This letter was made in his name
3375 And put into writing all by me.'
        The king commanded that it be
Handed to Botsard, his good clerk.*
There was none did better work
In that line than Botsard did.
3380 He it was who always read
The letters that the court received.
Brunel, the ass, and he retrieved
The pilgrim's sack from the neck of Beline,
Who would soon regret that he had been
3385 So stupid as to go astray
In talking and give himself away.
        Botsard took the sack, I said,
And when he drew forth Coward's head,
Reynard's crime was manifest.

* Botsard is the monkey. We know this from *Reinardus Vulpes*, where Balduinus calls him 'Boccardus simius'.

3390 He looked at it and thus addressed
Noble, the king: 'What letter is this?
My lord, upon my faith, this is
Coward's head. Alas, you gave
Too much credence to that knave,
3395 Reynard, the fox, your Majesty.'
    Then were clear, for all to see,
The grief and anger of king and queen.
The king stood with a dejected mien
And bowed his head to the ground.
3400 At last he raised it, and a sound,
The horriblest that ever was heard
To come from any beast or bird,
Came forth from him, that far and near
All the beasts were seized with fear.
3405   Then leapt forward Firapel,
The leopard. He knew King Noble well,
For he was of his kin and could afford
To speak to him thus: 'My King and Lord,
Why do you raise this big roar?
3410 Your show of grief could not be more
If the queen had passed hence.
Do behave and show some sense
And ease your sorrow for a spell.'
The king said, 'Sir Firapel,
3415 I cannot help being wrought up.
I have been led by a knavish pup
Into a snare so craftily
That I must hate the sight of me,
And my self-confidence is gone.
3420 The friends whom I could count upon,
Stalwart Bruin and Isengrim,
Those are by a fake pilgrim
Turned into such bitter foes

That my honour, if they chose,
3425   Even my life, might be at stake.'
In reply Firapel spake:
'He who did wrong ought to amend.
The wolf and Bruin, his brave friend,
And the lady Hersent as well,
3430   Must be paid for their fell,
Their shoes, their suffering, and pain
With the life of the ram Beline,
Since he confessed he had a share
In the betrayal of the hare,
3435   He did wrong and he shall pay.
And then we must, without delay,
Run after Reynard till he is caught
And hanged by the neck as the fellow ought,
Without trial or further plea.'
3440   The king replied, 'So let it be.
I approve, my Lord Firapel.
If that be done, I shall feel well,
As it will ease my grief somewhat.'
Said Firapel, 'My lord, it ought.
3445   I will go and make amends.'
      Firapel went to his friends,
The two in prison where they lay.
He first untied them, I dare say,
And then he spoke, 'My lords, I bring
3450   The peace and protection of the king.
He sends you greetings and his vow
That he is deeply sorry now
For the wrong he did to you.
He offers amends, if that will do,
3455   No matter who may praise or damn.
He will give you Beline, the ram,
And all his kin to be your prey

From now on until Doomsday.
They are yours, wherever they be,
3460 In the forest or on the lea;
You may slaughter them at will.
Also, the king won't take it ill
Nor regard it a felony
If you do harm or injury
3465 To Reynard and to all his clan,
Wherever you catch them, if you can.
This twofold peace His Majesty
Is willing to give to you in fee
Simple and free for ever and aye.
3470 And in return the king this day
Would have you swear him loyal support.
He also promises by no tort
Of his ever to wrong you more.
That is what Noble, the king, swore.
3475 Accept his oath, and live in his grace.
I would, if I were in your place.'
    Sir Isengrim spoke unto the bear:
'Sir Bruin, speak up, if you care.'
    Said Bruin, 'I would rather roam the plains
3480 Than be lying here in chains.
Let us go to Noble, the king,
And accept his offering
Of peace.' They went with Firapel
And made their peace. And all was well.

BIBLIOGRAPHY

MANUSCRIPTS

The text of Willem's poem has been preserved in two complete manuscripts, one in the Royal Library at Stuttgart (MS. A), the other in the library of Prince Alfred von Salm-Reifferscheidt, at Dyck, in the neighbourhood of Neusz (MS. F). The former, which is known as the Comburg manuscript because it belonged until 1805 to the Ritterstift Comburg am Kocher, is a large codex of 346 parchment folios of which verso 192 to recto 213 contain the Reynard poem. It is written in the dialect of East Flanders and dates from the early fifteenth century. The Dyck manuscript was copied c. 1340 by a scribe who spoke a more northern dialect, either that of Zeeland or of Holland. Two fragments, in the dialect of Brabant, are preserved in the library at Darmstadt. The text of these is closer to that of the Dyck than to that of the Comburg manuscript (MS. E). Because of the existence of a later and greatly expanded version, the text represented by MSS. A, F and E is usually referred to as Reynard I.

This later version, entitled *Reinaerts Historie* in the manuscript, consists of a revision of Willem's poem by a fourteenth-century imitator who has added a sequel to it, the two parts together running into 7,794 lines. This work, usually referred to as *Reynard II*, is extant in a late fifteenth-century manuscript written on parchment and preserved in the Royal Library at Brussels (MS. B). Six leaves of another manuscript on paper, each containing four columns of about forty-six lines are preserved in the Royal Library at The Hague (MS. O).

EARLY PRINTED BOOKS

1473

Reinardus Vulpes. A Latin-verse translation of Willem's poem made in 1272 by 'Balduinus nomine Juvenis, corpore Senex', a cleric of the diocese of Bruges. Not preserved in manuscript, but in an incunabulum of c. 1473 printed at Utrecht by Ketelaer and De Leempt. Diplomatic reprint by F. A. G. Campbell (The Hague 1859), critical edition by W. Knorr. (Eutin 1860).

1479

Die Hystorie Van Reynaert die Vos. A prose version of Reynard II, printed in 1479 by Gheraert Leeu at Gouda, and again in 1485 by Jacob Jacobszoon van der Meer at Delft. Edited and compared with Caxton's English translation by J. W. Muller and H. Logeman (Zwolle 1892). Caxton did not use Leeu's edition but either a manuscript or a printed text which was earlier and better than Leeu's. Both incunabula are preserved in two copies, the Gouda edition in the Royal Library, The Hague, and in the British Museum, the Delft one in the Municipal Library at Lübeck and in a private library at Brussels.

1481

The History of Reynard the Fox. William Caxton's translation of the prose version of 'Reynard's Story', printed by him at Westminster in 1481 and again in 1489. Editions by William J. Thoms for the Percy Society (London 1844), by Edward Arber in *The English Scholar's Library of Old and Modern Works* (London 1878), and by Edmund Goldsmid in the *Bibliotheca Curiosa* (Edinburgh 1884).

1487

Fragments of a printed edition (c. 1487) of 'Reynard's Story' (*Reynard II*) from the press of Gheraert Leeu at Antwerp. The text is divided into four books and these into chapters headed by captions, the work of a certain Henric van Alcmaer, who further added brief glosses and moralizations. Preserved at Cambridge, England, 222 lines in all. Diplomatic reprint by F. Prien in his edition of *Reinke de Vos*, pp. 267–273.

1498

Reinke de Vos. A Low German translation of Henric van Alcmaer's edition printed at Lübeck in 1498 by Barkhusen, who was himself the translator. Edited by F. Prien (Halle 1887).

1564

Reynaert de Vos een seer Ghenevcheliicke ende Vermakeliicke Historie, a sixteenth-century chapbook in prose printed at Antwerp by Peeter van Keerberghen in 1564. Edited by Ernst Martin (Paderborn 1877).

EDITIONS

1812

Die erste entdeckte Handschrift des Reineke Fuchs in flammändischer Sprache, her. von F. D. Gräter in *Odina und Teutona* pp. 276–375 (Breslau 1812). This is the first edition of the text in the Comburg manuscript, a very faulty one owing to the editor's insufficient knowledge of thirteenth-century Flemish.

1834

Reinhart Fuchs her. von J. Grimm. (Berlin 1834.)

1836

Reinaert de Vos, episch fabeldicht van de twaalfde en dertiende eeuw, met aenmerkingen en ophelderingen uitgegeven door J. F. Willems (Ghent 1836). The text of this edition is based upon that of Grimm.

1856

Van den Vos Reinaerde uitgegeven en toegelicht door W. J. A. Jonckbloet. (Groningen 1856.)

1874

Willems Gedicht Van den Vos Reinaerde und die Umarbeitung und Fortsetzung Reinaerts Historie. Her. und erläutert von Ernst Martin (Paderborn 1874). An excellent piece of German scholarship, which remained the standard edition for nearly half a century.

1887

Van den Vos Reynaerde, uitgegeven door W. L. van Helten. (Groningen 1887.)

Van den Vos Reynaerde. Nach einer Handschrift des XIV. Jahrhunderts im Besitze des Fürsten Salm-Reiffenscheidt herausgegeben von H. Degering. (Munster 1910.)

Van den Vos Reinaerde. Naar de thans bekende handschriften en bewerkingen critisch uitgegeven met eene inleiding door J. W. Muller. (Ghent 1914.) Muller has tried to reconstruct the original text by a painstaking collation of the manuscripts, the Latin text of Balduinus's *Reinardus Vulpes*, the Cambridge fragments of the printed edition of 1487, the prose version of Reynard II, the chapbook of 1564, and the Low German version of 1498. It is this edition which the present translator has followed.

Van den Vos Reynaerde. Uitgegeven naar het Comburgsche en Darmstadtsche handschrift door F. Buitenrust Hettema, naar het Dycksche handschrift door H. Degering. Zwolsche Herdrukken No. 18. (Zwolle 1921.)

The Cambridge Reinaert fragments, edited with an introduction and bibliography by Karl Breul. (Cambridge 1927.)

TRANSLATIONS

Willems, J. F. *Reinaert de Vos, naar de oudste beryming*. (Eecloo 1834.) Reprinted in *Keus uit de dicht- en prozawerken van J. F. Willems*, II, 1–103. (Ghent 1873.)

Delepierre, O. *Le Roman du Renard traduit pour la première fois d'après un texte flamand du XIIe siècle*, edited by J. F. Willems. (Brussels 1837.)

1844

Geyder, A. F. H. *Reinhart Fuchs, aus dem Mittelniederländischen zum erstenmal in das Hochdeutsche übersetzt.* (Breslau 1844.)

1847

Van Duyse, P. *Reinaert de Vos in zijn geheel en in de oorspronkelijke maat bewerkt.* (Ghent 1847.)

1874

De Geyter, J. *Reinaert de Vos in Nieuwnederlandsch.* (Schiedam 1874.)

1906

Stijn Streuvels *Reinaert de Vos, naar de handschriften van het Middeleeuwsche Epos herwrocht.* (*Wereldbibliotheek*, Nos XI–XII). (Amsterdam 1906.)

CRITICAL STUDIES

1861

Paris, P. *Les aventures de maître Renart et d'Ysengrin son compère, suivies de nouvelles recherches sur le Roman de Renart.* (Paris 1861.)

1863

Jonckbloet, W. J. A. *Étude sur le Roman de Renart.* (Groningen 1863.)

1884

Voigt. *Ysengrimus.* (Halle 1884.) An edition of the Latin poem by Nivardus* preceded by an excellent Introduction.

1884

Muller, J. W. *De oude en de jongere Bewerking van den Reinaert.* (Amsterdam 1884.)

1893

Sudre, L. *Les Sources du Roman de Renart.* (Paris 1893.)

* Nivardus is said to be the author in one MS. only, an anthology of aphorisms and maxims culled from *Ysengrimus*. But A. Van Geertsom has convincingly proved that the poet was Simon, Abbot of St Bertinus at St Omars.

1910

Foulet, L. *Le Roman de Renard.* (Paris 1910.)

1912

Teirlinck, Is. *De Toponymie van den Reinaert.* (Ghent 1910–1912.)

1917

Muller, J. W. *Critische Commentaar op Van den Vos Reinaerde.* (Utrecht 1917.)

1925

Vercoullie, J. *Diersage en Reinaert de Vos.* (Bruges 1925.)

1927

Sisam, K. *Introduction to 'Chaucer. The Nun's Priest's Tale'.* (Oxford 1927.)

LANCELOT OF DENMARK

A Fine Play of
Lancelot of Denmark
How he came to woo a damsel who was in his mother's service

I entreat God upon his throne, and the lovely maiden Mary, that they may always protect us, and so preserve us in virtue that we may gain the kingdom of Heaven; and this I pray of Mary, Heaven's queen, lady above all others.

Now listen to what will be played for you. It concerns a noble knight, who loved a damsel, fine and pure of heart; but still she was too humble in rank and in possessions for him. It enraged his mother against him that he loved beneath him; whenever he looked upon the lovely creature it filled his heart with joy, but his mother, that evil woman, became more and more angry and aggrieved, and constantly reproached him with abasing himself so. Always he excused himself, courteously, as he well knew how; yet still he showed loving favour to this beautiful girl, whose name was Sanderijn. Nothing could surpass her excellence; but yet she was too lowly for him, and this so infuriated his mother that in the end she struck at them.

Now I command you all to give heed to this, and to ponder it well, for I believe that you will never have heard a love story like it. Now I command you all, poor and rich, to keep silence and observe how it begins.

The action at first takes place in and about the castle of Lancelot of Denmark; then in the forest, or beside the castle of a knight who dwells in a land far off from Denmark.

(In the neighbourhood of the castle of Lancelot of Denmark)

LANCELOT Oh God my Lord, how can this be, that I have so lost my heart to the lovely Sanderijn? Day by day my mother upbraids me for loving so beneath me, and I must listen to many an angry word; but love has so pierced my heart that I cannot give her up, and whenever I see her I must speak to her. But this so aggrieves my mother that I must dissemble it. I will wait here under this eglantine for my love, for I know well that she will come soon to this orchard.

SANDERIJN (*entering*) Oh noble knight, so fine and true, may God, who rules over all this earth, bless this day for you, my noble, generous-hearted knight.

LANCELOT Oh lovely maid, may God be with us both, keeping us free from sin and from all harm, and especially guarding us from slanderous tongues. Let there be no evil rumours concerning us. Oh Sanderijn, give me your counsel. My heart is so shaken and so tormented with love for you that I fear lest it cost me my life. Oh Sanderijn, loveliest of women, if I cannot possess you I shall die and be eternally lost.

SANDERIJN Oh noble knight, so high in rank, that can never be; however much I may love you, I am not your equal. You are too great and too rich for me to be your lady. So this must now come to an end, for though I may love you with all my heart, I will not be the light-of-love of any man living under heaven, not though he were a king and wore a crown: still I would not so abase myself.

LANCELOT Oh lovely and pure-hearted maid, if only I could have my will, you would not be unrewarded, Sanderijn, choicest of women. Strange things can happen; and you might yet become my wife. Be kind to me, be true to me, and come with me into the castle; and I shall give you a jewel the like of which I believe you never saw.

SANDERIJN No, noble sir. I thank God upon his throne that I am still a virgin. Not if you wished to make me a gift of a thousand pounds of purest gold, my noble lord, my honoured sir: still I would preserve my honour. Sir Lancelot, so great in rank, even though I may possess little and come of no fine kin, still I will so conduct myself that I become no man's mistress. I will love honourably, and not behave myself like a peasant girl.

LANCELOT Sanderijn, I swear by Mary the virgin that I mean no churlish conduct towards you. There is no woman born under heaven, however rich or great or fair, who could exalt me as your love does. Oh, Sanderijn, are you going to leave me in this despair? Will you not have pity on me, shall I have no consolation, will you not come with me and sport in this green valley, while the young birds sing and the flowers blossom in the grass? Lovely maid, I mean no harm, I intend no churlish tricks!

SANDERIJN Sir Lancelot, many men say that 'Easy believing is often deceiving'. This is surely true and no lie at all, for all around one sees women brought into disgrace for trusting men too much, which afterwards they bitterly regret, when it is too late. I do not know the man born on earth whom I would trust so far as to go playing in the wood with him, lest he should have his pleasure of me.

LANCELOT I love you too dearly, Sanderijn, lovely creature, to dishonour your body, even had I the power. This was not what I intended, to offer you any harm. If we were strangers in a foreign land, I would give you all our food, Sanderijn my dearest, before I would let you suffer hunger. On my knightly honour, Sanderijn, I would do you no harm that could cause you sorrow.

SANDERIJN Sir Lancelot, we have been here too long: someone might hear us or see us. Scandalmongers are always on the lookout for some way of defaming others. Evil tongues would always rather tell a bad tale than a good one, for that is their nature. Let us part at once, and not give them matter for talking about us. Noble baron, excellent sir, may our Lord God protect you, and preserve you in virtue wherever you go. *(Exit)*

LANCELOT Alas, my heart is still sore for love of the beautiful Sanderijn. She will not let me have my way, and that will be a sorrow for the rest of my life. However much I groan or lament, she will not come to the forest with me. Her honour means more to her than any gold; I know that well by what she says. Her life is pure, her heart is noble. By my knightly state, I wish indeed that she were born my equal; however little she possessed, I would make her my wife, for her life is pure and her heart is wholly honour-able. But she will not be moved to pity me, and this fills my heart with great grief.

HIS MOTHER *(entering)* Lancelot of Denmark, I have been listen-ing to your wooing, and by the Virgin, I am amazed that you do not set more store by yourself, that you will give your love so basely: you act like a madman, moaning about someone who cares nothing for you. Are you not ashamed to disgrace yourself so, loving a woman so lowly born?

LANCELOT Oh, mother, her life is so pure, her heart is so noble, and she is so lovely that I must love her till I die. My heart is all aflame whenever I see her. My lady, my dear mother, I must love her whatever happens.

HIS MOTHER Lancelot, will you not consider who you are—your noble estate, your high degree—will you not do as I counsel, and love one who is your equal?

LANCELOT There is no woman in all Christendom whom I would prefer before Sanderijn. If only she were mine! Dear mother, be content: if all the world were at my disposal, I would still wish her to be my wife.

HIS MOTHER Wretch that you are, be ashamed to disgrace your-self so! How many lovely young ladies are there of high birth and great lineage—and you have to love one who is base!

LANCELOT Ah, mother, the power of love pays no respect to high birth or riches: love looks into another's heart for love, so that out of two there may become one. I have often heard it said that love looks for love: let one be poor, the other rich, still love will have its way. True love pays no heed to riches or high degree, nor did it ever, for all is brought about by fortune. Love is noble, and cannot be constrained: and love is no respecter of persons.

HIS MOTHER Oh, Lancelot, how utterly you have set your heart on Sanderijn! If you will act as I wish, I shall make her yours to-night, my fine knight, all in secret in your chamber, to do all that your heart longs for; but you must make me one promise.

170

LANCELOT By St Simeon, lady mother, I will promise whatever you wish, if only she and I may be together in my chamber.

HIS MOTHER Lancelot, promise me upon your honour as a knight that when you have had all your will with Sanderijn, you will say 'I have had enough, Sanderijn, I am sick of you and I have had my fill; and it is as if I had gorged myself on seven roast pigs.' You must not forget: these are the very words which you must say, and then you must turn away from her and sleep soundly for the rest of the night, without saying another word.

LANCELOT Oh mother, is this what you want, that I should say anything so gross? I have never heard the like of it. What good can it do you for me to say this to Sanderijn, and then lie sleeping like a dog, without speaking to her again, as if I were a knave? What would that pure creature think of me, who have sworn my love to her, if I were to use her so disgracefully? I would die of grief.

HIS MOTHER Lancelot, this is what I want; and if you are to possess her, you must promise it and perform it like a man of good faith.

LANCELOT Then let her come to me, and I will do as you wish, even though it breaks my heart. *(As he goes off)* 'What many say they do not mean.' This is my case now, for whatever my tongue may say, my heart will not assent to it, for I love her for her virtues. I pray to God, the Lord of all, that she may not be grieved by this, for she is so honourable and so good that if she takes it amiss her heart will grow cold to me, and so my heart will still be in torment. *(Exit)*

HIS MOTHER And now I have done all that I need to part the two of them. Do you not see how he would disgrace himself, he, the noblest in the land, loving a woman so basely born? If I would permit it the scoundrel would marry her, I know very well; but I shall arrange things differently, so that it never happens. Where are you, Sanderijn, my pretty girl? Come here, I wish to speak to you.

SANDERIJN *(entering)* Here I am, most noble lady: tell me what is your wish.

HIS MOTHER Sanderijn, I am in great distress, and I must tell you of my sorrow. It is my dear son Lancelot, who has been taken very ill; last night he fell sick, and since then he has not spoken one word. I do not know what is the matter with him, or what it is that makes him suffer; but this morning, as dawn broke, he gave one heavy sigh. Sanderijn, I am afraid for his life, and my heart is full of grief. Now, Sanderijn, my pretty maid, I beg you to go to Lancelot, lying there in such pain, because I am so anxious for him.

SANDERIJN Noble lady, I will gladly do as you ask, at once. I will go, as my love for you commands, for it would be an affliction to me if anything were to harm him. *(Exit)*

HIS MOTHER Those who order their affairs in good time can live long in honour. This is how to contrive to bring a woman into a trap; and who could have done it better than I? For once he has had his will, his love will cool. We see that happening every day.

(An interval. Then enter Sanderijn from Lancelot's chamber)

SANDERIJN Oh God, who let yourself be crucified, what treacherous creature is Lancelot's mother? I understand this far better now than I did last night. She told me a wicked lie when she said that he had been taken ill, to trap me by making false seem true, and so she brought me into Lancelot's power, which I shall rue for the rest of my days. And yet what torments me more than all is the words that that fine knight spoke to me as he turned his face from me as if I had been a stinking cur. This had pierced me through and through; but he shall never have good or ill of me again. I will forsake everything, and go lamenting my own way into some foreign land. I pray to God to hide the disgrace which I have received, for my mind is filled with sorrow. Lancelot, you will never see me again. I shall go into the forest to make my lament.

172

(In a forest surrounding the castle of a knight in a far-off land)

SANDERIJN *(entering)* Oh Father, Son and Holy Spirit, I pray you to protect my body, so that I may never have commerce with any man to my disgrace: whatever land I may be in, let me remain as I am. I pray for this to you, mother and gentle Virgin, fountain of all chastity: let no man ever again offer insult to me. This is my prayer to you, fountain of virtue, holy mother and maiden pure. And over there I see a lovely spring, and by it I will rest. I have been fasting for so long that I am consumed with hunger and thirst, and I can no longer endure my craving to drink.

A KNIGHT *(entering)* Now in God's name I will go out hunting; and I beg him enthroned on high, and Mary that lovely maid, that they protect me today, and give me grace and good fortune, so that I may hunt and make a kill. Truly, it is so long since I have caught anything that I am ashamed. I have been hunting for four days, and I have not even taken a rabbit. My heart is full of shame to have wasted my labours so. But now I will blow my horn, and see if God will guide me.

(He blows his horn)

In the name of the Lord who made me, I see some beast stirring over there. This is consolation to my heart, for never did anyone see a finer prey than stands there by the spring. But it looks to me like a beautiful maid, and a chaste one. Oh my Lord God, if I might capture her, I should not have wasted my time! I will sound my horn again and see what she will do.

(He blows his horn again)

Oh God, Lord above all, give me the good fortune to gain this lovely creature for my own! Oh lovely maid, stand still, for you must be my captive. I would rather catch you than a boar made

173

of pure gold. I thank God that I rose this morning in time to hunt so well.

SANDERIJN Oh noble and most excellent knight, do not treat me as a churl would. I appeal to your nobility not to misuse me, for that would be your disgrace wherever you went in the world. You seem to me to be a knight of great renown, and so I pray you, noble lord, that you will not ill-treat me, but leave me as I am.

THE KNIGHT Tell me, lovely woman, where did you come from into this forest? I am astonished to find you alone like this, here in the wood beside this spring. What is the reason for your distress? Has someone made an assignation with you here, and are you waiting for him, lovely one? Perhaps he is a man of such authority that I should not be speaking to you.

SANDERIJN Oh noble knight, oh worthy lord, I am not waiting here for any man. The reasons why I am here are quite different. I have wandered away from my own land, where once I lived in honour and happiness. I do not know where I am, and I stand here in great dread, and I do not know where I am going, and I lament before God my misfortune and the miseries which this world makes me suffer.

THE KNIGHT Now I thank God that I rose early today to meet such good fortune, and that I have hunted to come upon so fine and beautiful a quarry. God has brought us together: that I know now for sure. You were made for me, for there is nothing about you which does not delight me. Your lovely form, your courtly speech, every part of you is a joy to me. We will have fine sport together, so come with me into my castle; you have never seen the like of the jewel which I possess and which shall be yours.

SANDERIJN Sir knight, I implore you by the great God to cease such talk as this, and not to make a mock of me, for I am all forlorn in this land.

THE KNIGHT Lovely creature, my heart burns and consumes in the fire of love: you are so courtly and so beautiful that I swear on my honour as a knight that you shall be my wife for your beauty, if only that is according to your good will. I beg you, tell me your name, for truly you shall be my lady!

SANDERIJN Noble knight, if what you say is true I shall tell you my name. I am called Sanderijn, and my father was called Robert, and he was well born, a knight-at-arms, and he served with the king of Averne.

THE KNIGHT Oh lovely maiden, how happy it makes me to hear that you come of knightly stock. Again I thank God for my good fortune, that today I did not lie in bed. It was an angel who called me and bade me go hunting in the forest. Never did my eyes look upon a lovelier woman, and truly you shall be my wife.

SANDERIJN Sir knight, if that is your will I shall gladly confide myself to you, and I thank God and you for the honour you do me in stooping so far beneath your own rank. You have spoken so lovingly to me, in such courtly and fair terms, that I pray God to reward you for it, for that courteous heart that prompted you to speak now so kindly to me.

THE KINGHT Then, fair maiden, let us go, that I may pledge my fidelity to you.

SANDERIJN First let us wander in this garden, sir knight, and let us talk together for a while; and I beg you to give good heed to what I say. Look at this fine and leafy tree, and at all its lovely blossoms, whose scent suffuses all this garden. Well may it bloom so beautifully, standing in so fair a valley; and with its beauty and its fragrance it makes all this garden more lovely still. Supposing, now, that a fine falcon were to fly among its branches and to perch on one of them, and to pluck one of its flowers, and never to come near it again, so that it never had more than that one flower: would you despise the tree because of this, and have it felled and sold for timber? This is what I ask you now, to speak the truth to me, noble knight, as courtesy demands.

THE KNIGHT Fair lady, I understand you very well. What is one flower, so long as no more were taken? That is no reason for me to hate the tree, and order it to be cut down. It is too beautiful for that; and I see it all covered with blossoms, and there is good hope that it will yield fine fruit if that be the will of God. Now let us never speak of this again; but come with me, my lovely lady. *(Exeunt)*

(In Lancelot's castle, or in its neighbourhood)

LANCELOT Alas, alas, now all my joy is gone, all that I ever prized upon earth, for nowhere can I discover where she is, my all too lovely Sanderijn. Accursed be my mother, for I should never have spoken the words if it had not been for her. I felt as if my heart were breaking when I uttered those cruel words; and that is why she stole away, all in secret, and left me. I shall never find peace again until I look upon that noble creature, that pure being whom I love so much that I think that I shall die for want of her. To be with her is life itself, for she is all beauty, she is the paragon of women and the mistress of my five senses. There is no man living could love a woman so much as I love her. I shall have her searched for through all Christendom, till I know where she can be. Where are you, Reynald? Come here, dearest of all my serving men.

REYNALD *(entering)* Oh noble lord, why do you stand here grieving so?

LANCELOT Alas, I have never known sorrow to equal this, now that I have lost that lovely creature Sanderijn. It feels as if my heart would crack for the great woe that I am suffering. I am amazed that I have not gone out of my mind; and I would rather be dead than never to see her again. Reynald, you must go and seek out everywhere, to see if you can find her, for I shall never know another moment's joy until I look upon her with my own eyes. Reynald, be faithful to me now, and search for her high and low; and when you find her, tell her that I shall make her my bride, whatever my family may do.

176

REYNALD Sir, I will risk my very life for you, and shrink from no labour; but perhaps it would be better for you to forget all this. What do we know of how she may be living?

LANCELOT Oh no, she is all honour and purity, and I know well that she would not abase herself for all the riches of the earth. Of this I am sure, for she is a most noble lady. Reynald, if you love me truly, make all haste, and search for her east and north, south and west, and go on seeking until you find her. My eyes never looked upon another woman whom I loved so.

(The forest surrounding the castle of the Knight in a far-off land)

THE KNIGHT'S FORESTER I have good reason for complaining; all these years I have roamed this forest, keeping my lord's game and guarding his preserves, constantly I have been in this vale and passed by this fountain, day by day and hour after hour, and never once have I had the good luck to find a woman here. Have I not good cause to complain, that I have never had the chance even to see one, but yesterday, when my lord rose and set off to hunt in the woods, he found a woman here, lovelier than I have ever seen? Courteously he took her by the hand, and brought her to his castle, full of joy. If she had been an empress she could not have been a more noble creature. Her name is Sanderijn, and he has made her his wife. No one need wonder that I am aggrieved that the like of this has never happened to me; but by God, I shall keep my eyes open from now on, early and late. If ever I could catch a pretty prey like that I should be pleased enough, and I would thank God for it every day of my life. I shall hide myself behind this thicket, and see what comes my way.

(About one year later. Reynald enters the forest surrounding the castle of the Knight in the far-off land)

REYNALD *(entering)* Oh Mary, mother and maiden pure, I pray you now to guide me well and to bring me news, good and true, about Sanderijn, for my lord Lancelot has lost all peace of heart, and is so tormented with love for her that it cannot long continue so. He has sworn his oath as a knight to make her his wife if only he can find her, for he is so filled with sorrow for the loss of her that he lives in great woe, all for true love. Oh God my Lord, how glad I would be if only I could find her! But Lord, what is the meaning of this, who is the man standing over there, and what does he want? He looks to me so savage, and he carries a great heavy club. I am sure that he is a murderer, unless I am much mistaken. All the same, I shall ride up to him, for he seems to be alone, and I never yet saw a man by himself who could frighten me. My friend, God bless you on this fine morning, and grant you good health every day of your life!

THE FORESTER My friend, God reward you, whoever you may be, for your kind words to me.

REYNALD Now, as you are a true man, tell me this. In these last years, have you ever seen a damsel, lovely and gracious, passing this way?

THE FORESTER Friend, understand me well. I have kept this forest for many a day, but I never yet saw any woman here, young or old, believe me; but just about a year ago my lord, who is a fine knight, rose up early one morning and came hunting by this fountain, and here he found a pure young damsel hiding. He made her his captive, his heart full of joy, and he said that he had hunted well to trap a maiden so lovely and well born as she.

REYNALD Friend, tell me more about this; and I beg you to tell me what her name was.

THE FORESTER Friend, I will tell you the truth. Her name is Sanderijn; and no one could be nobler or lovelier than she. There is no lady living in this land to compare with her, for she is as good as she is beautiful. My lord has made her his wife, for she is faithful to him and obedient and submissive; and everyone here who is of my lord's kin loves her for her great virtue. Every man living in this castle is full of joy on her account.

178

REYNALD May God now counsel me what I should do! This is the very damsel that I mean, and I have sought for that pure lady up and down in many a country, yet never till I met you could I hear any news of her. Oh, my dear friend, tell me now, how can I contrive to speak to her?

THE FORESTER Friend, that you can never do; or, if you want to talk to my lady, it can only be if I help you, for I am her trusted servant, and the senior among all the serving men whom my lord keeps here. Now, if you were to put the price of a drink into my hand, I would arrange it so that you could talk to her to your heart's content, my noble warrior.

REYNALD The price of one drink is soon spent, and there is little to show for it. Run off as fast as you can, and make it possible for me to talk to Sanderijn; and here are two pieces of gold for you. Tell her as plainly as you can that there is a messenger here from Denmark who must speak to her at once.

THE FORESTER I will make all speed, and bring the lady back with me. *(He goes off towards the castle.)* Oh noble, generous lady, humbly I ask you to approach, for there is a valiant knight standing outside who is anxious to converse with you. *(Exit. Enter Sanderijn)*

REYNALD Oh noble lady, faithful and virtuous, may God, ruler of all, bless you this day, lovely maid Sanderijn.

SANDERIJN Reynald, you are welcome. Tell me what it is you want.

REYNALD I will tell you, excellent lady. You are to come with me, for that fine knight Lancelot has had you searched for everywhere, and his last words to me were to command that if I could find you I should bring you back, for it is his will to make you his bride.

SANDERIJN Reynald, my friend, that game is over now. Tell him to play it with someone else. I would not give a straw for Lancelot's love.

REYNALD Oh, lovely lady, if only you could see the state that he is in! His sorrow is bitter indeed. Since he lost you, my noble lady, it has never ceased to torment him, and he has lived in cruel woe. It will certainly be the death of him if he does not win you back again, for I know well that he loves you better than the whole world. He has sworn his knightly oath that as soon as you are found he will make you his wife, however little his family may like it.

SANDERIJN Reynald, we are wasting our time to talk like this. I live here honourably and well, and I am married to a noble man, whom I love better than I love life itself. I would not leave him for anything. If Lancelot were as great as Hector of Troy, if it pleased God to endow him with the very crown that King Alexander once wore, still he would have nothing to offer to me. My husband alone is dear to me, who has shown me all courtesy, and I shall always be faithful to him.

REYNALD Oh, Sanderijn, most lovely lady, if Lancelot cannot regain you, the rest of his life will be sorrow and torment. You may regret for ever that you have made this marriage, for without doubt the noble Lancelot would have married you.

SANDERIJN There is no cause for me to regret, nor shall I ever, for I never found so honourable a man on earth as is my husband. He well merits my love, for he is a knight of great repute, valiant, noble-hearted, well born and well endowed; prudent and wise, a famous warrior known for his great deeds. I love him with my whole heart, more than any other creature. Now I will not stay any longer. Reynald, return with all speed, and tell your lord, Lancelot, never to think of me again.

REYNALD Oh noble and generous lady, if this is how it must be, I beg you, my excellent mistress, to give me some sign so that I may truly show that I have seen and spoken with you.

SANDERIJN You shall have what you ask for, Reynald. I will give you a sign, for you alone, which will be clear and good. Tell that fine knight that once he and I stood in a fair orchard, and that a splendid falcon came flying by in all its might, and lighted upon a branch that was full of blossoms. Tell this to your good knight, and say that the falcon who flew down then took one blossom from the bough, and let all the others be. Then he beat his pinions and flew off at great speed. Tell all this to that noble lord, and say that soon afterwards the falcon came back, and flew up and down, seeking that same branch, but he could never find it again. This filled the falcon with great grief, never to be able to find the bough. Tell this to that valiant warrior, and then he will well believe that you have seen me and talked to me, when you relate this story to him. This is all I have to say. Reynald, may God guard you.

(Sanderijn goes back to the castle)

REYNALD Oh God, now I must go and leave that lovely lady behind me. I have no notion how I am to carry out this errand. If I tell Lancelot the whole truth, that she is alive and well at her ease, I know well that it will bring harm to us all, for he will still long for the beautiful creature. I know, if it were to cost him his life, and if he had to risk the life of everyone who is kin to him, however distant—I know well what will happen, and how many will suffer cruel death on this account; and it will all be in vain, for there is nothing to be gained. It would only bring endless misery to Lancelot and everyone who fought at his side. I will choose my words carefully, and say that she is dead.

(In Lancelot's castle and its neighbourhood)

REYNALD *(entering)* Where are you, noble lord, most valiant knight of Denmark?

LANCELOT *(entering)* Welcome, Reynald, my dear friend, welcome indeed. Tell me, what news have you of Sanderijn?

REYNALD Oh noble and most generous lord, I searched for her in many a land, until at last I found the lovely creature in a city called Ravast, in Africa, to which she had travelled. Lancelot, my fine and noble knight, when I discovered the beautiful Sanderijn and spoke to her about you, it cost her her life, for her noble heart broke at once when she heard your name spoken.

LANCELOT Reynald, this is an empty tale, and I can clearly tell that you are lying to me. Do not deceive me, but tell me the truth. I would be better able to believe you if you had brought me some clear sign from her.

REYNALD Lancelot, my prince, I will tell you, and you alone, a sign which is clear and good which that pure woman gave to me. She told me that once you two, all alone, were standing in a fair green orchard, and that a fine and noble falcon came flying by in all its splendour, and lighted upon a bough which was all grown with lovely blossoms. This is what she told me to say, good knight: that the falcon which perched there took one blossom from the bough and left all the others alone, and then beat his pinions and flew off at great speed. This is what she told me, noble lord: that the falcon came back again and sought up and down for that bough, but it never could find it again. This filled the falcon full of great sorrow, never to be able to find the bough. This is the sign that excellent lady gave me, brave warrior, and then she turned her face from me and spoke no more.

LANCELOT Oh Queen of Heaven, oh almighty Lord, that is the sign, and it is clear and good, and I can well believe that it is true. Tell me, then, Reynald, is she dead?

REYNALD Yes, my noble lord, and buried in the earth. *(He goes to one side)*

LANCELOT Oh, Sanderijn, you were the bough, so lovely in all its blossoms, and I was the falcon, I know well, who plucked one flower from it, for I have never known peace again since I lost that noble bough, and I have been in endless torment for you, my one true love. All joy upon earth is sorrow to me now, mirror of all women, wherever they be in this world! Now may I well cry 'Alack! alack!' for the mother who bore me, since her false heart rejoiced when she gave me that evil counsel. Alas for that cruel deed, alas for the lamentable words which she made me speak, and which lost me that lovely maiden, and which now will cost me my life, for my heart is utterly defeated, and I would that it might break in two, that I might make an end of this life; for wherever I may go on earth I shall be joyless to the end of my days. I set my heart in all honour upon a maid, but I lost her through false counsel; and now my heart is so afflicted that I shall die of pure grief. I trust that I may see her in heaven, and in that hope I am happy now to die. Oh, merciful God of Heaven, take into your keeping her soul and mine, for now life will have no more of me. *(He dies)*

EPILOGUE

REYNALD You lords and ladies, you women and men, take example from this. If anyone loves truly, and gains his true love, let him use courteous language to her; for this noble man of Denmark was falsely counselled to speak ill to his love, and it was that which brought this harm to him, and in the end he paid for it with his noble life, for he loved that fair one more than life itself. The evil counsel which was given to him made him speak ill to her, and so true love was blighted, and she fled away from him. So I advise you above all else, each man of you, to speak courteously whenever you can, and, in particular, to use courteous language about all women, and to love them truly; and so you will have joy of them.

SAY THAT AGAIN

THE HUSBAND Oh dear, oh dear, time passes slowly for men like me, nagged to death every day of our lives and never knowing a minute's peace! If I go out I can have fun, but that's all over the minute I get home, for I live a dog's life in my own house. My wife scolds and curses at me until I wish that I were dead; and yet, to tell the truth, it serves me right, because sometimes I laugh till I weep at the way she sets about me.

THE NEIGHBOUR Well, neighbour, how are you?

THE HUSBAND My good neighbour, how do you think I am, with an ill-tempered wife like mine?

THE NEIGHBOUR Is she as bad as ever?

THE HUSBAND More's the pity for me, she is: you might as well try to stop a hen from scratching.

THE NEIGHBOUR But have you never tried?

THE HUSBAND I might as well try to catch the moon in a bucket.

THE NEIGHBOUR Well, I'll give you good advice, and if you follow it she'll change her tune.

THE HUSBAND Make her change her tune? Believe me, I've tried it.

THE NEIGHBOUR Have you tried shouting at her, have you tried being nice to her?

THE HUSBAND I've tried everything I know: I've been nasty, I've been kind, and much good it did me.

THE NEIGHBOUR Does she still keep on at you?

THE HUSBAND God knows, she does; and she gets worse every day.

THE NEIGHBOUR Well, I'll give you a few words of good advice.

THE HUSBAND Do you think it will do any good?

THE NEIGHBOUR I swear it will.

THE HUSBAND Then tell me what it is.

THE NEIGHBOUR Now listen carefully. When you go home, whatever happens, whether she nags at you, whether she hits you, whatever she does, just say: 'Say that again!'

THE HUSBAND I don't see what good it will do me, saying that to her. If I said 'Say that again' to her every time she lugs me around and clouts me and pushes me, she'd murder me! A lot of help that would be! 'I'll give it to you, you and your "Say that again"!' —I can just hear her saying it.

THE NEIGHBOUR Don't you worry about what will happen: you just stick to it through thick and thin.

THE HUSBAND And am I just to say 'Say that again'?

THE NEIGHBOUR Yes, you must, just that and nothing else.

THE HUSBAND My God, I'll be saying 'Say that again' for the rest of my life.

THE NEIGHBOUR If you want to change her, just learn to say 'Say that again', and stick to it.

THE HUSBAND Why should I make more trouble for myself than I've got? If she gives me a clout and I say 'Say that again', she'll only clout me a dozen times over. What am I supposed to do then?

THE NEIGHBOUR Suppose she offered you a nice cake, baked with all the spices in it that you like, couldn't you say 'Say that again'?

THE HUSBAND Indeed I could. I'd keep on saying 'Say that again', if she would offer me some decent food.

THE NEIGHBOUR Well, there you are. I promise you, just make up your mind and stick to the plan, and soon you'll have her so frightened she'll think you are going mad.

THE HUSBAND Well, good for you, if this is how to get myself free.

THE NEIGHBOUR It is: just say 'Say that again'!

THE HUSBAND You bet! I swear by every saint, I'll say 'Say that again' whatever she does to me.

THE NEIGHBOUR And then I'll come and tell her that she's knocked you silly, that you're possessed with the devil and that it's all her fault for ill-treating you so.

THE HUSBAND This is going to be a grand joke!

THE NEIGHBOUR Now off with you: get back home as fast as you can!

THE HUSBAND That's right, neighbour: I'm off, so goodbye.

THE NEIGHBOUR Go on, go on, and I'll keep my fingers crossed that you don't give in; because she's bound to be surprised, and then there will be an almighty row.

THE HUSBAND Well, off I go, and God help me.

(He goes home)

Well, let's sit down and have our dinner. Where the devil are you?

THE WIFE Well, now, welcome at last to his gracious lordship! Where have you been till this time of day, I'd like to know?

THE HUSBAND Say that again.

THE WIFE Be off with you: I'll soon show you what's what!

THE HUSBAND Say that again.

THE WIFE Shut up! May God curse you for having lived so long, you old fool!

THE HUSBAND Say that again.

THE WIFE Have you gone off your head? 'Say that again'—is that all you can say?

THE HUSBAND Say that again.

THE WIFE Will you listen to what I have to put up with? He's driving me mad with his 'Say that again'!

THE HUSBAND Say that again.

THE WIFE I hope that God punishes you for this! What do you think you're doing, you nasty wretch?

THE HUSBAND Say that again.

THE WIFE Do you hear the way he's going on? Is he never going to say anything else?

THE HUSBAND Say that again.

THE WIFE Will you stop it, this 'Say that again', devil take you?

THE HUSBAND Say that again.

THE WIFE Now I'm warning you, I'll settle you so that you'll be sorry for yourself!

THE HUSBAND Say that again.

THE WIFE This is the very devil himself: no one need doubt it, I'm sure of that.

THE HUSBAND Say that again.

THE WIFE Stop it! You nasty beast, what are you trying to do to me with this 'Say that again'?

THE HUSBAND Say that again.

THE WIFE I might just as well talk to myself! I'll give you something to shout about!

THE HUSBAND Say that again.

THE WIFE I'll give you such a hiding, you'll be glad to stop your 'Say that again'.

THE HUSBAND Say that again.

THE WIFE Can't you do anything to help it? I've never heard anything like it in all my life!

THE HUSBAND Say that again.

THE WIFE My God, I'll make you sing a different tune, see if I don't!

THE HUSBAND Say that again.

THE WIFE By God, I will, I promise you! Will you stop, or won't you?

THE HUSBAND Say that again.

THE WIFE Oh, oh, I've beaten him till my arm aches. It was your mother's bad luck that you were born, and it's mine too. What game are you up to?

THE HUSBAND Say that again.

THE WIFE This is the maddest thing that I've ever heard of!

THE HUSBAND Say that again.

THE WIFE I'll get someone to see to you. Stop it—don't say 'Say that again' once more!

THE HUSBAND Say that again.

THE WIFE What on earth can he mean? I've never heard anything so strange in all my born days.

THE HUSBAND Say that again.

THE WIFE Jack, I'll run out of this house! *(Exit)*
   Good neighbour, come and help me!

THE NEIGHBOUR What is the matter, neighbour dear?

THE WIFE I'll tell you what's the matter. Whatever I say to my
   husband, good or bad, all he ever says to me is 'Say that again'.

THE NEIGHBOUR I'd get the priest to him if I were you. It's plain
   that he's gone off his head; and that's because you clout him all
   the time.

THE WIFE Do you really think we ought to fetch the priest?

THE NEIGHBOUR By God, I do.

THE WIFE Then let's go look for him.

THE NEIGHBOUR I'll be glad to come with you and find him.
   (Exeunt)

THE HUSBAND This is the way to handle nagging wives! By St
   John, it was good advice that I should say 'Say that again'. My
   wife may be a terror, but I've been a match for her this time. It
   makes me laugh, that she thinks I've gone mad. That's her mistake—I'm wiser than Solomon was, and Virgil and Aristotle
   along with him. It was a good idea to say 'Say that again': this is
   the way to cure her evil temper. Just like a cuckoo, I'll go on
   singing, 'Say that again' and that will bring me happiness. She
   thinks that she has got the better of me, but she'll learn better before we're finished. *(Exit)*

THE WIFE Good sir, please come and see what is wrong with my
   husband.

THE PRIEST Why, what is the matter with him?

THE WIFE He just keeps on saying 'Say that again'.

THE PRIEST That's a bad sign. 'Say that again'—what ill can that
   forbode?

THE NEIGHBOUR It is plain that he's gone off his head. His wife
   has knocked him about and clouted him, till I'm sure that he has
   gone into this decline.

THE PRIEST I'll go with you and look at him. You carry my stole
   and my book and my holy-water sprinkler.

THE NEIGHBOUR This is going to be a grand affair: now we shall get to the bottom of this 'Say that again'.

THE PRIEST Come along, let us make haste. *(Exeunt)*

THE WIFE Look, sir, this is my house, and that is my husband. Speak to him.

THE PRIEST In the name of the Father and of the Son—

THE HUSBAND Say that again.

THE WIFE I tell you, he's got a devil in him—I am sure of it.

THE HUSBAND Say that again.

THE PRIEST Is that all he ever used to say—'Say that again'?

THE WIFE Oh, no, sir: he's only started it just now.

THE PRIEST My friend, I warn and counsel and admonish you for your own good, and I conjure you, by every creature that can harm you, by the spectres that ride by night, by the hob-goblins that make church bells to ring, by cockatrices and water-sprites and spooks, and by the trolls that fly in storms, and by the cats that dance upon the Sabbath, and by the flying witches, that you tell me truly what it is that afflicts you.

THE HUSBAND Say that again.

THE PRIEST Is that all that you can say?

THE WIFE No, sir, it's not, believe me.

THE PRIEST Now, Jack, I must warn you again. By the two trees which were the sun and the moon, which prophesied Alexander's doom, and by every dead priest and by all that great company lying dead in Babylon's fortress—

THE HUSBAND Say that again.

THE PRIEST Well, God alone knows what can stop him—I don't!

THE NEIGHBOUR Supposing we gave him something to eat?

THE PRIEST Yes, yes, give him the best stew and roast meat you have.

THE WIFE I've got a nice piece of pasty here: shall I see if he would like it?

THE HUSBAND Say that again.

THE NEIGHBOUR Hurry up, don't lose time, get him to eat something and he'll be cured.

THE HUSBAND Say that again.

THE PRIEST I don't think there can be much wrong with him: he looks like eating the lot.

THE HUSBAND Say that again.

THE PRIEST I think he's going to be cured: he doesn't seem to me to be in any great trouble.

THE NEIGHBOUR Woman, this is all your fault. If you would feed your husband properly and not take your temper out on him, there wouldn't be anything the matter with him.

THE HUSBAND Say that again.

THE PRIEST You'll just have to pamper him for a while.

THE WIFE I will, sir, as much as I can; and I'll ask his pardon for all the harm I've done him. Jack, forgive me for being so bad-tempered and so bad to you!

THE HUSBAND I forgive you, with all my heart.

THE NEIGHBOUR There, now, what do you think of that? He's cured, this very minute.

THE WIFE Jack, are you all right: are you all right, Jack?

THE HUSBAND I'm quite all right, if you don't start your nagging again.

THE WIFE No, I won't, never again!

THE PRIEST Now God be praised that this evil has departed from the man. Goodbye, goodbye.

THE WIFE Sir, God go with you: you have taken a load from my heart this day. Let me show you the way. (*Exeunt the Wife and the Priest*)

THE NEIGHBOUR Now that your wife is out of the way we can talk safely. Well, wasn't that good advice I gave you, to say 'Say that again'?

THE HUSBAND By St James, it was; but I got well clouted for it at first.

THE NEIGHBOUR Yes, but afterwards you got some good pasty to eat.

THE HUSBAND Yes, that I did.

THE NEIGHBOUR I never saw any woman better taken in! The next time she tries to shove you around, or starts nagging at you, just try saying 'Say that again'.

THE HUSBAND By St Anthony, I shall: it's the only way I've ever found to get some peace.

THE NEIGHBOUR And as long as she's worried whether you are cured or not, you'll be the top dog in this house. *(Enter the Wife)*

THE WIFE Oh, you two beasts, if only someone would slaughter the pair of you! I've heard every word you said!

THE HUSBAND Oh my God, I'm done for now!

THE NEIGHBOUR Murder! Help! This woman's trying to kill us!

THE WIFE Now let's have 'Say that again'!

THE HUSBAND I'll never say it again in all my life, I promise you, my dear.

THE WIFE Will you say it again?

THE HUSBAND No, I swear, I never will! It was he, our neighbour, who told me to do it.

THE NEIGHBOUR It wasn't I who told you, Jack: you must bear me out!

THE WIFE And didn't you know what a fool he is? He couldn't cut a tree down without cutting off his own hand!

THE NEIGHBOUR Well, I know it now!

THE WIFE Then just watch out!

EPILOGUE

Let every man who wishes to fare well take heed,
and may the grace of God protect us every one,
and may the Father, the Son and the Holy Spirit
grant to us blessedness beyond compare.